196766
UCB

Welcome

Welcome to the 31st edition of Condé Nast Johansens Recommended Hotels & Spas, Great Britain & Ireland.

Your feedback via e-mails, letters and our website across the past 12 months has been invaluable in assisting us to maintain the highest standards from our selection of recommended hotels and spas throughout Great Britain and Ireland. It has always been our policy to professionally inspect every Recommendation every year, and this applies just as much today as it did to the first Derek Johansen Guide in 1982. No property can appear in our Guide unless it meets our exacting standards.

D1612288

You will have n[illegible] ountry hotels where the focu[illegible] ion" offering a diverse choic[illegible] "experience" rather than just accommodation and good food.

Amongst the following pages you will find many examples of the extra activities now available to guests. Here are some that appeal to me: foraging for your breakfast with the Chef at Lime Wood, Hampshire; staying in a luxurious tree house at Chewton Glen, Hampshire; falconry at Ashford Castle, County Mayo; driving a classic car at Holbeck Ghyll, Cumbria; wine courses at Penmaenuchaf Hall, Gwynedd.

You can share your experiences by giving Condé Nast Johansens Gift Vouchers to your friends and family. The vouchers can be redeemed at any of our 2013 Recommendations and make a much valued gift for anniversaries and other special occasions. Buy them at www.condenastjohansens.com/gift-vouchers

Nominations for our annual Awards for Excellence are based on your feedback by e-mail or letter. However, you can simply click on the "Vote" button located on each hotel's online page entry or contact us via "Tell us about your stay" at the foot of each hotel page entry on www.condenastjohansens.com

Finally, don't forget to mention that you are a Condé Nast Johansens Guide user when making an enquiry or booking. You should receive a very warm welcome when you arrive.

Wishing you safe and happy travels!

Andrew Warren
Managing Director

41, London, England, p75

Natural Beauty
From the South of France

Experience L'OCCITANE amenities in the best properties around the world.
L'OCCITANE is proud to be a Condé Nast Johansens preferred partner.

About this Guide

Recommendations and Regional Maps:

Mini Listings:

To find a hotel by location:

- Use the **county maps** at the front of the Guide to obtain a page number for the area of the country you wish to search.
- Turn to the **index by location** at the back of the Guide, which start on page 182.
- Alternatively, use the **maps** at the front of each country section where each hotel is marked.

If you cannot find a suitable hotel you may decide to choose one of the properties within the Condé Nast Johansens Recommended Small Hotels, Inns & Restaurants Guide. These more intimate establishments are listed on pages 149-153.

Once you have made your choice please contact the hotel directly. Rates are per room, including VAT and breakfast (unless stated otherwise) and are correct at the time of going to press but you should always check with the hotel before you make your reservation. **When making a booking please mention Condé Nast Johansens as your source of reference.**

Readers should be aware that by making a reservation with a hotel, either by telephone, e-mail or in writing, they are entering into a legal contract. A hotelier under certain circumstances is entitled to make a charge for accommodation when guests fail to arrive, even if notice of the cancellation is given.

Combe House, Devon, England – p53

Recommendations can be found plotted on more detailed maps at the front of each country section

SCOTLAND
N. IRELAND
IRELAND
WALES
ENGLAND
Cumbria p43
Durham p61
North Yorkshire p115
Conwy p142
Denbighshire p143
Cheshire p36
Derbyshire p51
Lincolnshire p74
Gwynedd p144
Staffordshire p101
Rutland p100
Ceredigion p140
Powys p146
Worcestershire p114
Warwickshire p111
Northamptonshire p99
Pembrokeshire p145
Herefordshire p72
Bedfordshire p30
Gloucestershire p62
Buckinghamshire p34
Hertfordshire p73
Bath & NE Somerset p28
Berkshire p31
London p75
Wiltshire p112
Hampshire p68
Devon p52
Dorset p57
West Sussex p106
East Sussex p102
Cornwall p37
Channel Islands
Jersey p14
UCB
196766

Key to Symbols

- 23 Total number of bedrooms
- The property participates in a minimum of 3 environmentally-friendly practices specified by Condé Nast Johansens
- The property is owner managed
- The property is available for exclusive use
- The property is situated in a quiet location
- Wheelchair access – we recommend contacting the property to determine the level of accessibility for wheelchair users
- The property has a chef-patron (the owner of the property is also the chef at the restaurant)
- M 23 Maximum capacity for meeting/conference facilities on-site
- 8 Children are welcome, with minimum age where applicable
- Dogs are welcome in bedrooms or kennels
- At least 1 bedroom has a four-poster bed
- Some or all bedrooms provide an iPod docking station
- ISDN/modem point available in all bedrooms
- WiFi Wireless internet connection available in most rooms
- Smoking is allowed in some bedrooms
- A lift is available for guests' use
- Air conditioning is available in all bedrooms
- Gym/fitness facilities are available on-site
- SPA The property has a dedicated spa with on-site qualified staff and an indoor pool, offering extensive body, beauty and water treatments
- Indoor swimming pool on-site
- Outdoor swimming pool on-site
- Tennis court on-site
- Walking – details of local walking routes, an overnight drying room for clothes and packed lunches can be provided by the property
- Fishing on-site
- Fishing can be arranged nearby
- Golf course on-site
- Golf course is available nearby
- Shooting on-site
- Shooting can be arranged nearby
- Horse riding on-site
- Horse riding can be arranged nearby
- H The property has a helicopter landing pad
- The property is licensed for wedding ceremonies

Barnsley House, Gloucestershire, England– p64

Condé Nast Johansens Preferred Champagne Partner

For further information please contact sole UK agents:
Hatch Mansfield on +44 (0) 1344 871800 or Email info@hatch.co.uk

www.taittinger.com

Exclusive COFFEE & TEA...Explore your tastes...

Chez-Toi®

AT HOME

We at Café du Monde are proud to present Chez Toi.

Since 1989 our Coffees and Teas have been served exclusively in renowned Hotels and Restaurants where quality is paramount. With Chez Toi they are now available for you to explore...

Coffee Introduction Box

Contains:

4 of each individual 2 cup cafetière sachets.

El Salvador - Monte Sion
Ethiopian - Yirgacheffe
Kenyan - AA Grade
Brazilian - Monte Cristo
Jamaican - Blue Mountain
Colombian - Exelso
Sumatra - Takengon

Tea Introduction Box

Contains:

Great Taste Award winning Newby Teas.

Enveloped 1 cup teabags.

12 x English Breakfast
12 x Assam
12 x Ceylon
12 x Jasmine Blossom

call us on

01322 284804

for your special Condé Nast Johansens price

www.cheztoi.co.uk

Café du Monde is the preferred coffee partner to Condé Nast Johansens

51 Buckingham Gate, Taj Suites and Residences, London, England - p98

Condé Nast Johansens Ltd, 6-8 Old Bond Street, London W1S 4PH
Tel: +44 (0)20 7499 9080 Fax: +44 (0)20 7152 3565
E-mail: info@johansens.com www.condenastjohansens.com

Hotel Inspectors: Tim Fay, John Morison, Mary O'Neill, Andrew Warren
Production Manager: Kevin Bradbrook
Production Editor: Laura Kerry
Designer: Tyrel Smythe
Marketing Manager: Adam Crabtree
Digital Marketing Manager: Gemma James
Copywriters: Stephanie Cook, Sasha Creed, Debra O'Sullivan

Client Services Director: Fiona Patrick

PA to Managing Director: Amelia Priday
Managing Director: Andrew Warren

Whilst every care has been taken in the compilation of this Guide, the publishers cannot accept responsibility for any inaccuracies or for changes since going to press, or for consequential loss arising from such changes or other inaccuracies, or for any other loss direct or consequential arising in connection with information describing establishments in this publication.

Recommended establishments, if accepted for inclusion, pay an annual subscription to cover the costs of inspection, the distribution and production of copies placed in hotel bedrooms and other services.

No part of this publication may be copied or reproduced, stored in a retrieval system or transmitted, in any form or by any means, electronic, mechanical, photocopy, recording or otherwise, without the prior permission of the publishers.

The publishers request readers not to cut, tear or otherwise mark this Guide. No cuttings may be taken without the written permission of the publishers.

Copyright © 2012 Condé Nast Johansens Ltd.
Condé Nast Johansens Ltd. is part of The Condé Nast Publications Ltd.
ISBN 978-1-903665-63-3
Printed in Scotland by Scotprint, Haddington.
Distributed in the UK and Europe by Roundhouse Group, Brighton, Sussex (bookstores). In North America by Casemate Publishing, Pennsylvania (bookstores).

A British love affair

We all have a love affair with sleep, yet many of us never truly experience a deep uninterrupted night's sleep, night after night. At Hypnos each Royally Approved bed is individually handmade by master craftsmen using the finest natural materials to guarantee years of sumptuous and rejuvenating slumber. So, to be sure that you have the very best night's sleep and awake feeling revitalised and refreshed, visit a Hypnos Retailer and choose a Hypnos bed that's just right for you. Hypnos – the God of Sleep.

Hypnos, Great Britain's first carbon neutral bed maker, is proud to be Condé Nast Johansens Preferred Partner for beds and mattresses.

www.hypnosbeds.com

Awards for Excellence

Whatley Manor, Wiltshire, England – p113

The Winners of the Condé Nast Johansens 2012 Awards for Excellence

The Condé Nast Johansens 2012 Awards for Excellence were presented at the Condé Nast Johansens Annual Dinner held at The May Fair hotel, London, on 7th November 2011. Awards were given to properties from all over the world that represent the finest standards and best value for money in luxury independent travel. An important source of information for these awards was the feedback provided by guests who completed Condé Nast Johansens Guest Survey Reports.

Please nominate a hotel via its online page entry on www.condenastjohansens.com under "Tell us about your stay".

2012 Winners appearing in this Guide:

Most Excellent Hotel
Chewton Glen – Hampshire, England, p70

Most Excellent Waterside Hotel
The Grand Hotel – East Sussex, England, p102

Most Excellent City Hotel
The Egerton House Hotel – London, England p89

Most Excellent Country House Hotel
Lime Wood – Hampshire, England, p69

Most Romantic Hotel
Combe House – Devon, England, p53

Most Excellent Family Friendly Hotel
Calcot Manor Hotel & Spal – Gloucestershire, England, p67

Most Excellent Hotel Spa
Coworth Park – Berkshire, England, p31

Most Excellent Restaurant
'The Dining Room' at Whatley Manor – Wiltshire, England, p113

Most Excellent Bedroom
The May Fair – London, England, p92

Most Excellent Value For Money
The Spread Eagle Hotel & Spa – West Sussex, England, p109

Champagne Taittinger Wine List Award
The George Of Stamford – Lincolnshire, England, p74

Channel Islands

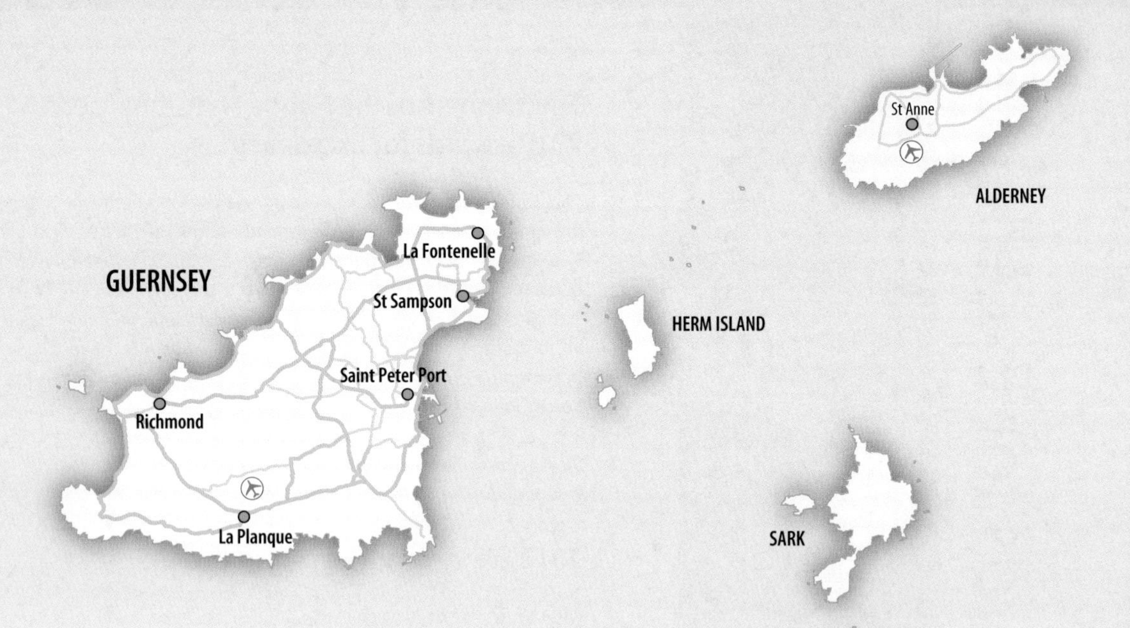

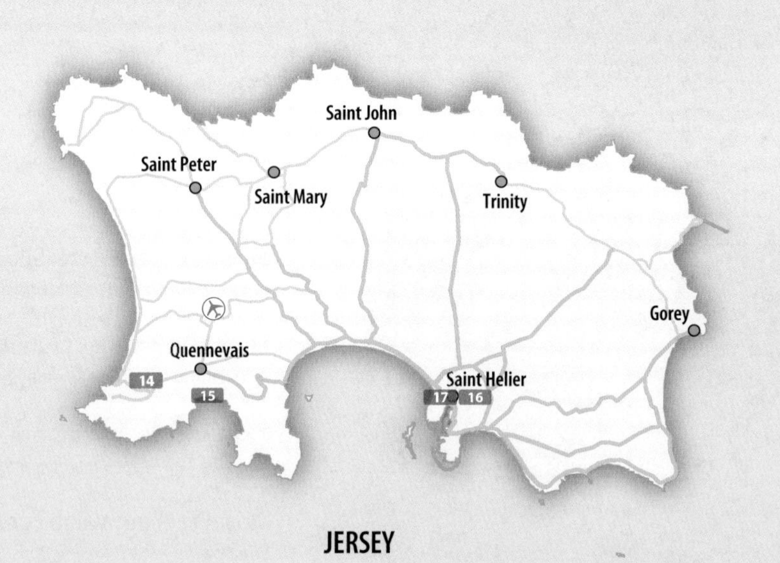

For further information on the Channel Islands, please contact:

Visit Guernsey
Tel: +44 (0)1481 723552
E-mail: enquiries@visitguernsey.com
www.visitguernsey.com

Jersey Tourism
Tel: +44 (0)1534 448800
E-mail: info@jersey.com
www.jersey.com

Sark Tourism
Tel: +44 (0)1481 832345
E-mail: office@sark.co.uk
www.sark.co.uk

Aurigny Air Services
Tel: +44 (0)1481 822886
E-mail: res@aurigny.com
www.aurigny.com

Flybe
Tel: 0871 700 0123
E-mail: reservations@flybe.com
www.flybe.com

Condor Ferries (UK)
Tel: 0845 609 1024
E-mail: reservations@condorferries.co.uk
www.condorferries.com

Isle of Sark Shipping Company
Tel: +44 (0)1481 724059
E-mail: info@sarkshippingcompany.com
www.sarkshippingcompany.com

or see **pages 155-158** for details of local historic houses, castles and gardens to visit during your stay.

For additional places to stay in the Channel Islands turn to **pages 149-153** where a listing of our Recommended Small Hotels, Inns & Restaurants Guide can be found.

The Royal Yacht Hotel, Jersey, Channel Islands – p17

The Atlantic Hotel

LE MONT DE LA PULENTE, ST BRELADE, JERSEY JE3 8HE
Tel: 01534 744101 **International:** +44 (0)1534 744101
Web: www.condenastjohansens.com/atlantic **E-mail:** reservations@theatlantichotel.com

The Atlantic Hotel is the object of continuous and thoughtful investment by its owner who places the needs of his guests first. Be spoiled by excellent service and admire the contemporary interior decorated with vibrant island art. The Atlantic stands in 6 acres of private grounds alongside La Moye Golf Course with sympathetic cliff-top landscaping that has opened a vista, allowing an uninterrupted view of the ocean across a 5-mile sweep of St Ouen's Bay. Enjoy a special treat and stay in the prestigious Atlantic Suite with its own entrance hall, living room, guest cloakroom and service pantry. Gaining a much deserved Michelin Star, the restaurant showcases modern British cuisine, with an emphasis on seafood and fresh local produce. Be sure to book in advance.

Our inspector loved: *The complete experience of superb service, sublime food and ocean sunsets!*

Price Guide:
single £110–£160
double £160–£360
suite £360–£560

Awards/Recognition: Condé Nast Johansens Most Excellent Waterside Hotel 2010; 1 Star Michelin 2012; 4 AA Rosettes 2012–2013

Location: A13, 0.5 miles; St Helier, 5 miles; Jersey Airport, 3 miles

Attractions: Durrell Wildlife Conservation Trust; Eric Young Orchid Foundation; Jersey War Tunnels; La Mare Vineyards

St Brelade's Bay Hotel

LA ROUTE DE LA BAIE, ST BRELADE, JERSEY JE3 8EF
Tel: 01534 746 141 **International:** +44 (0)1534 746 141
Web: www.condenastjohansens.com/stbreladesbayhotel **E-mail:** info@stbreladesbayhotel.com

Our inspector loved: *The comfortable, newly decorated interiors, the views of St Brelade's Bay and the family-friendly atmosphere.*

Price Guide:
standard £140-£238
sea view balcony £186-£284
bay suite £246-£344

Location: A13, 0.5 miles; St Helier, 5 miles; Jersey Airport, 3 miles

Attractions: Durrell Wildlife Conservation Trust; Eric Young Orchid Foundation; La Mare Vineyards; The Jersey War Tunnels

With a truly special location overlooking one of the Channel Island's most beautiful sandy beaches, this historic hotel has a reassuringly traditional exterior. First opened in the 19th century, it underwent a comprehensive refurbishment in 2011 and continues to offer its warm welcome to guests. The 74 rooms range from 1 and 2-bedroom suites to superior and family rooms, while many of the superb sea view rooms have balconies, as do the garden rooms, which look across the 5 acres of stunning gardens. All coolly capture the essence of the hotel's much loved, sophisticated yet comfortable atmosphere, and feature fresh fruit on arrival, LCD TVs and 24-hour room service. Dining is a treat at St Brelades, and The Bay restaurant is a destination in itself. The creation of modern Jersey-inspired dishes starts with quality local produce, and light meals can also be enjoyed al fresco at the more casual pool-side Petit Port Café.

THE CLUB HOTEL & SPA, BOHEMIA RESTAURANT

GREEN STREET, ST HELIER, JERSEY JE2 4UH
Tel: 01534 876500 **International:** +44 (0)1534 876500
Web: www.condenastjohansens.com/theclubjersey **E-mail:** reservations@theclubjersey.com

The Club Hotel & Spa reflects the real buzz that exudes from St Helier itself. Furnished with contemporary design and understated luxury in mind, bedrooms and suites are decorated to an exceptionally high standard you'll love: LCD TVs, CD players and sleek bathrooms featuring granite surfaces, power showers and all-enveloping sumptuous bathrobes are standard features. The sophisticated Bohemia Restaurant has rapidly gained an enviable reputation with Head Chef Shaun Rankin, participant in BBC2's Great British Menu 2009, at the helm. Private dinner parties up to 24 and a chef's table for 6 can be accommodated here. Visit the hotel's chic, popular bar, and savour a slower pace of life at the Club Spa by indulging in a treatment. Once refreshed, why not take a walk along the sandy beaches, surf, sail or explore the secret places of this beautiful island.

Our inspector loved: *The contemporary style and exceptional dining experience.*

Price Guide:
double/twin from £99
suite from £295

Awards/Recognition: 1 Star Michelin 2012; 4 AA Rosettes 2012-2013

Location: A15, 0.25 miles; Jersey Airport, 5 miles

Attractions: Shopping in St Helier; Maritime Museum; Jersey Pottery; Elizabeth Castle and Harbour

The Royal Yacht Hotel

WEIGHBRIDGE, ST HELIER, JERSEY JE2 3NF
Tel: 01534 720 511 **International:** +44 (0)1534 720 511
Web: www.condenastjohansens.com/theroyalyacht **E-mail:** thereception@theroyalyacht.com

Our inspector loved: *The view from the Penthouse Terrace.*

Price Guide:
gold double £185-£205
platinum double £230
penthouse suite £650-£750

Location: Opposite the Harbour at Weighbridge Square; St Helier; Jersey Airport, 5 miles

Attractions: Sailing Packages; German War Tunnels; Jersey Zoo; Shopping

Overlooking the harbour, this luxuriously contemporary hotel brings an exuberant atmosphere to Jersey's idyllic St Helier, and boasts lively bars, fine food and the sumptuous Spa Sirène. Many of the hotel's guest rooms have balconies so you can fully appreciate the views, and all are decorated in a warm, contemporary style. For an extra treat book a Penthouse Suite and unwind in the Jacuzzi on your private terrace! As for dining, eating out on Jersey is part of the culture and "fresh" here means from the ocean or the open countryside. The three restaurants, Restaurant Sirocco, the brasserie-style Café Zephyr and The Grill all reflect this ethos with chic, perfectly cooked menus and the chance to dine al fresco. Drinks, from traditional beers to cocktails, are served in three easy-going, fun bars, each with their own ambience. Then there's Spa Sirène with expert therapists on-hand in the beautiful surroundings for pampering treatments that will restore mind, body and soul.

North West England

North East England

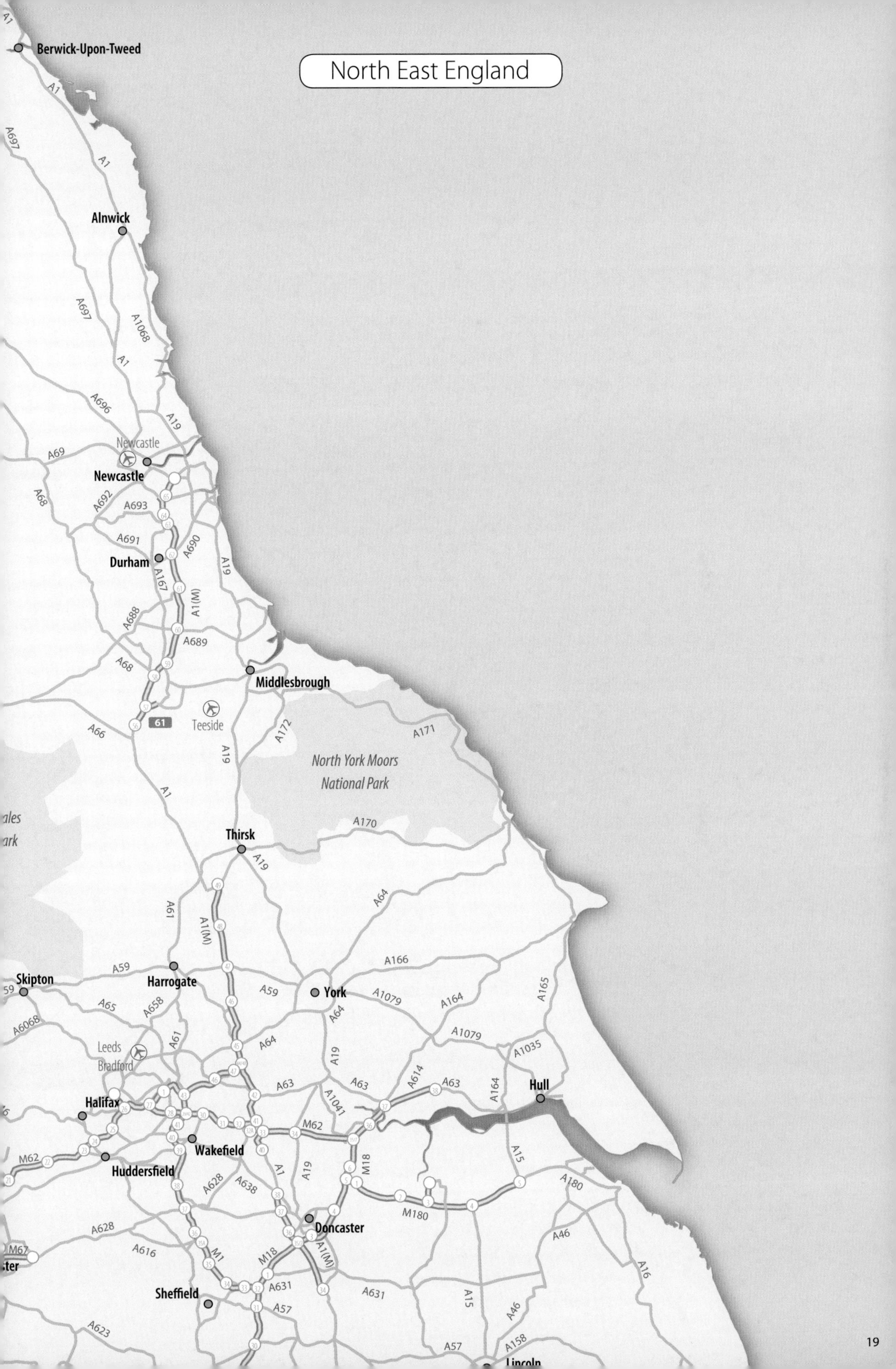

Central England

Eastern England
Louth
Lincoln
Cromer
King's Lynn
The Broads
Great Yarmouth
Norwich
Peterborough
Thetford
Newmarket
Bury St Edmunds
Cambridge
Ipswich
Felixstowe
Bishop's Stortford
Stansted
Colchester
Luton
Chelmsford
M180
A46
A16
A158
A15
A17
A52
A1121
A151
A1101
A47
A148
A140
A1065
A1122
A134
A10
A11
A146
A143
A1066
A12
A605
A1 (M)
A142
A141
A14
A428
A6
A1
M11
A505
A421
A131
A120
A133
A602
A414
A130
M1
A5
M25
A406
A127
74
99
30

South West England

South West England
WALES
Exmoor
National Park
Bristol
Bath
Warminster
Taunton
Yeovil
Blandford
Forum
Exeter
Bridport
Dorchester
Weymouth
Torquay
Kingsbridge
M5
M4
A38
A37
A4
A46
A4174
A361
A39
A36
A350
A303
A358
A354
A377
A30
A35
A380
A385
A429
A48
65
67
113
112
28
29
53
55
59
60
54

Southern England
Milton Keynes
Brackley
Stow-on-the-Wold
Cheltenham
Aylesbury
Luton
Oxford
Cirencester
Swindon
Reading
Windsor
Heathrow
Marlborough
Newbury
Basingstoke
Guildford
Winchester
Salisbury
Southampton
New Forest
Chichester
Portsmouth
Bognor Regis
Bournemouth
Cowes
Isle of Wight
M1
M3
M4
M5
M25
M27
M40
A3
A27
A31
A34
A36
A40
A41
A44
A303
A338

South East England
Felixstowe
Colchester
Stansted
Hertford
Chelmsford
City
GREATER
LONDON
Dartford
Sheerness
Ramsgate
Canterbury
Maidstone
Tonbridge
Gatwick
East
Grinstead
Royal
Tunbridge
Wells
Ashford
Dover
Folkestone
Uckfield
Hastings
Brighton
Newhaven
Eastbourne
A10
A505
A1(M)
A602
A414
M11
A120
A131
A12
A14
A133
A130
M25
A127
A13
A2
A20
M20
M2
A249
A299
A28
A256
A229
A22
M23
A26
A2070
A259
A272
A23
A21
A27
110
103
107
105
104
102

London, England
Central London
Hadley Wood
Wimbledon Common
Richmond -upon-Thames
Kingston
M11
M25
M40
M4
M3
97
Camden Town
Grand Union Canal
Kings Cross
St Pancras
Kings Cross St Pancras
Mornington Crescent
Euston
Euston Square
Warren Street
Great Portland Street
Regent's Park
Baker Street
Madame Tussaud's
London Zoo
Regent's Park
Primrose Hill
Marylebone
Edgware Rd
St John's Wood
Lords Cricket Ground
Swiss Cottage
Maida Vale
Kilburn Park
Warwick Ave
Paddington
Royal Oak
Westbourne Park
Bayswater
Queensway
Notting Hill
Notting Hill Gate
Holland Park
Lancaster Gate
Kensington Gardens
Hyde Park
The Serpentine
Marble Arch
Bond Street
Oxford Circus
Piccadilly Circus
Green Park
Mayfair
St James's Park
Buckingham Palace
Hyde Park Corner
Knightsbridge
Victoria & Albert Museum
Science Museum
Natural History Museum
South Kensington
Gloucester Road
High Street Kensington
Kensington
Kensington (Olympia)
Earl's Court
West Kensington
Chelsea
Sloane Square
Belgravia
Victoria
Pimlico
Tate Gallery
Vauxhall
Westminster
Westminster Abbey
Houses of Parliament
London Eye
Waterloo
Lambeth North
Elephant & Castle
Kennington
Borough
London Bridge
Tower Pier
Tate Modern
South Bank
River Thames
Embankment
Charing Cross
Temple
Blackfriars
Mansion House
Cannon Street
Monument
Bank
St Paul's
St Paul's Cathedral
Barbican
Farringdon
Chancery Lane
Holborn
Covent Garden
Leicester Square
National Gallery
Tottenham Court Rd
Goodge St
British Museum
Russell Square
Bloomsbury
Moorgate
Liverpool Street
City
Aldgate East
Shoreditch
Grand Union Canal
KINGSLAND ROAD
HIGH ST
COMMERCIAL ST
TOWER BRIDGE ROAD
OLD KENT ROAD
GREAT DOVER STREET
LONG LANE
BOROUGH HIGH ST
WALWORTH ROAD
NEW KENT ROAD
KENNINGTON ROAD
KENNINGTON LANE
ALBERT EMBANKMENT
LAMBETH PALACE RD
WATERLOO RD
BLACKFRIARS ROAD
SOUTHWARK BRIDGE
LONDON BRIDGE
VICTORIA EMBANKMENT
STRAND
KINGSWAY
HIGH HOLBORN
GRAY'S INN ROAD
EUSTON ROAD
HAMPSTEAD ROAD
TAVISTOCK PL
TOTTENHAM CT RD
SHAFTESBURY AVE
CHARING CROSS RD
WHITEHALL
PICCADILLY
REGENT STREET
OXFORD STREET
PORTLAND PLACE
MARYLEBONE ROAD
BAKER STREET
PARK LANE
EDGWARE ROAD
BAYSWATER ROAD
KENSINGTON ROAD
CROMWELL ROAD
BROMPTON ROAD
SLOANE STREET
KINGS ROAD
VAUXHALL BRIDGE RD
BUCKINGHAM PALACE ROAD
GROSVENOR PL
CONSTITUTION HILL
KENSINGTON CHURCH ST
EARLS COURT ROAD
HOLLAND PARK AVENUE
WESTWAY
MAIDA VALE
KILBURN HIGH ROAD
WELLINGTON ROAD
PRINCE ALBERT ROAD
78
75
76
77
79
80
82
83
84
85
86
87
88
89
90
91
92
93
94
95
96
98
A1
A10
A2
A200
A41
A502
A40

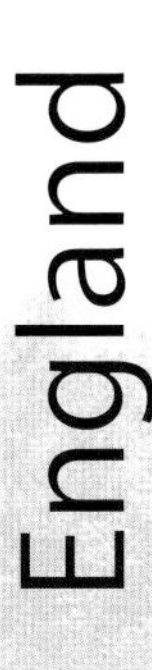

For further information on England, please contact:

Visit England
www.visitengland.com

Cumbria Tourist Board
Tel: +44 (0)1539 822222
E-mail: info@cumbriatourism.org
www.cumbriatourism.org

Heart of England Tourism
Tel: +44 (0)1905 887690
E-mail: tourism@visitheartofengland.com
www.visitheartofengland.co.uk

Visit London
Tel: 0870 156 6366
www.visitlondon.com

North East England Tourism Team
www.visitnortheastengland.com

North West Tourist Board
www.visitenglandsnorthwest.com

South East Tourism
www.visitsoutheastengland.com

South West Tourism
E-mail: info@swtourism.org.uk
www.visitsouthwest.co.uk

Welcome to Yorkshire
E-mail: info@yorkshire.com
www.yorkshire.com

English Heritage
Tel: +44 (0)870 333 1181
www.english-heritage.org.uk

Historic Houses Association
Tel: +44 (0)20 7259 5688
E-mail: info@hha.org.uk
www.hha.org.uk

The National Trust
Tel: 0844 800 1895
E-mail: enquiries@nationaltrust.org.uk
www.nationaltrust.org.uk

or see **pages 155-158** for details of local historic houses, castles and gardens to visit during your stay.

For additional places to stay in England turn to **pages 149-153** where a listing of our Recommended Small Hotels, Inns & Restaurants Guide can be found.

Gilpin Hotel & Lake House, Cumbria, England – p47

Dukes Hotel

GREAT PULTENEY STREET, BATH, SOMERSET BA2 4DN
Tel: 01225 787960 **International:** +44 (0)1225 787960
Web: www.condenastjohansens.com/dukesbath **E-mail:** info@dukesbath.co.uk

Dukes Hotel is a charming and relaxed Grade 1 town house hotel, full of character and style. This is evident as soon as you walk through the elegant entrance below half-moon shaped decorative glass, edged by slim, black, wrought-iron railings. Built from Bath stone, the hotel is a former Palladian mansion, and today basks in a sense of understated luxury. Most guest rooms and suites have original intricate plasterwork and large sash windows, and from front rooms you can see more Palladio-inspired façades, while those at the back look out to rolling hills. The 2 AA Rosette-awarded Cavendish Restaurant is light, airy and relaxing, and you can enjoy the best organic and free-range British ingredients, including Cornish lamb, local Somerset beef and seafood delivered daily from Devon.

Our inspector loved: *The comfortable town house rooms, hearty breakfast and the city on your doorstep.*

Price Guide:
single £99–£125
double/twin £159–£199
suite £179–£239

Awards/Recognition: 2 AA Rosettes 2012-2013

Location: A36, 0.5 miles; M4 jct 18, 8 miles; Bristol Airport, 15.5 miles; London, 90-min train

Attractions: Roman Baths & Pump Room; Thermae Bath Spa; Theatre Royal; Bath Abbey

The Royal Crescent Hotel & The Bath House Spa

16 ROYAL CRESCENT, BATH, SOMERSET BA1 2LS
Tel: 01225 823333 **International:** +44 (0)1225 823333
Web: www.condenastjohansens.com/royalcrescent **E-mail:** info@royalcrescent.co.uk

Our inspector loved: *The excellent and friendly service, and beautiful secret gardens.*

Price Guide:
single from £200
double/twin £220–£345
suite £470–£935

Awards/Recognition: Relais & Châteaux; 2 AA Rosettes 2012-2013

Location: City Centre; A4, 1.5 miles; M4 jct 18, 10 miles; Bath Spa Station, 1 mile

Attractions: Lady Sophina River Launch; Thermae Bath Spa; The Roman Baths; Prior Park National Trust House and Gardens; Lacock Abbey

Hidden in the middle of one of the great architectural masterpieces of Europe, The Royal Crescent Hotel, part of the prestigious Relais & Châteaux collection, is far more remarkable than a collection of buildings. Taking a short break in Somerset at this award-winning, luxurious hotel offers an opportunity to experience gracious living from the age when Bath was the centre of the civilised world. The Grade 1 listed buildings, built by John Wood the Younger, have been carefully restored to their original splendour. The individual bedrooms are rich in period features alongside 21st-century comforts. Beyond the main mansion stretches an acre of hidden garden and 4 original coach houses where The Dower House fine dining restaurant and The Bath House, a spa specialising in holistic treatments can be found. If all that is not enough, enjoy a Champagne cruise along the Kennet and Avon waterway in the hotel's private river launch.

LUTON HOO HOTEL, GOLF & SPA

THE MANSION HOUSE, LUTON HOO, LUTON, BEDFORDSHIRE LU1 3TQ
Tel: 01582 734437 **International:** +44 (0)1582 734437
Web: www.condenastjohansens.com/lutonhoo **E-mail:** reservations@lutonhoo.co.uk

Our inspector loved: *The traditional yet relaxed atmosphere and fabulous afternoon tea.*

Price Guide:
double/twin £230-£395
suite £495-£895

Awards/Recognition: Condé Nast Johansens Most Outstanding Service 2011; 2 AA Rosettes 2012-2013

Location: A1081, 1 mile; M1 jct 10, 3 miles; Luton Airport, 10-min drive; London, 30-min train

Attractions: Central London; Hatfield House and Gardens; Woburn Abbey Safari Park; Knebworth House

The sweeping drive that leads up to Luton Hoo builds a sense of excitement as you arrive at this impressive Grade I listed historic mansion. Restored to its original splendour it sits overlooking 1,000 acres of Bedfordshire parkland and formal gardens once designed by Capability Brown. Remarkable care has been taken with the restoration of the stonework and with the soft furnishing of silks, panelling and marquetry. The master bedrooms in the mansion house give a luxurious glimpse of the past. More contemporary bedrooms are to be found in the outbuildings close by: the Parklands and Flower Garden. Take tea in the Italianate drawing room or experience the elegance of the former state dining room, now the Wernher Restaurant. There is plenty to occupy you including the spa, a challenging 18-hole golf course and tennis courts.

Coworth Park

BLACKNEST ROAD, ASCOT, BERKSHIRE SL5 7SE
Tel: 01344 876600 **International:** +44 (0)1344 876600
Web: www.condenastjohansens.com/coworthpark **E-mail:** info.coworthpark@dorchestercollection.com

Our inspector loved: *The wonderful service, contemporary décor and beautiful spa, all within 40 minutes' drive from London.*

Price Guide: (room only, excluding VAT)
stable superior £215-£500
mansion superior £275-£575
suite from £335

Awards/Recognition: Condé Nast Johansens Most Excellent Hotel Spa 2012

Location: A30, 5 min drive; M3 jct 3, 10 miles; M25 jct 13, 5.5 miles; Gatwick Airport, 45 miles; Heathrow Airport, 20-min drive

Attractions: Windsor Great Park; Legoland; Windsor Castle; Wentworth Golf Course

Coworth Park, Dorchester Collection's luxury country house hotel and eco-luxury spa, is idyllically set within 240 acres of picturesque parkland on the borders of Windsor Great Park. This special luxury hotel features a seamless combination of traditional architecture, contemporary interior design, exquisite bespoke furniture and impeccable service. Put your feet up safe in the knowledge that you will be well looked after and take the time to appreciate each of the three restaurants' unbridled passion for exceptional cooking. In fact, Coworth Park has appointed one of the UK's most talented chefs, Brian Hughson, who brings with him more than 20-years' culinary experience at top London restaurants. Whether you are planning a wedding, conference, board meeting or incentive group, Coworth Park offers you a choice of meeting and private dining facilities. Golf enthusiasts are also in for a treat with the world-class Wentworth Golf Club located nearby.

Cliveden

TAPLOW, BERKSHIRE SL6 0JF
Tel: 01628 668561 **International:** +44 (0)1628 668561
Web: www.condenastjohansens.com/cliveden **E-mail:** info@clivedenhouse.co.uk

Cliveden is one of the world's finest luxury hotels. A grand stately home set in the heart of the Berkshire countryside surrounded by magnificent formal gardens. From the moment you enter the beautiful Great Hall with its grand fireplace, oak panelling and priceless artworks, you will feel like a treasured, personal guest, treated to the very highest standards of quality conveyed in the excellence of every detail. Where else can you be surrounded by such extraordinary extravagance and remarkable refinement, and at the same time feel so welcomed and at ease. Set amidst 376 acres of National Trust parkland, yet conveniently near to London and Heathrow Airport, Cliveden is set high above the River Thames, which affords the house with panoramic views over the beautiful grounds and beyond. Enjoy award-winning cuisine, a luxury spa, idyllic river cruises and state-of-the-art meeting room facilities.

Our inspector loved: *The wonderful history and beautiful surroundings of this very special country house hotel.*

Price Guide: (excluding VAT)
double/twin £210-£600
suite £540-£1290

Awards/Recognition: 2 AA Rosettes 2012-2013 (The Terrace Dining Room)

Location: A4, 3 miles; M4 jct 7, 4 miles; Heathrow Airport, 12 miles

Attractions: Windsor Castle; Windsor Great Park; Ascot Racecourse; Henley; Legoland

The French Horn

SONNING-ON-THAMES, BERKSHIRE RG4 6TN
Tel: 01189 692204 **International:** +44 (0)1189 692204
Web: www.condenastjohansens.com/frenchhorn **E-mail:** info@thefrenchhorn.co.uk

Our inspector loved: *The beautiful riverside location, excellent food and service that make The French Horn a timeless classic.*

Price Guide:
single £125–£170
double/twin £160–£215

Awards/Recognition: 2 AA Rosettes 2012-2013

Location: A4, 1 mile; M4 jct 10, 3 miles; Reading, 3 miles; Heathrow Airport, 20 miles

Attractions: Henley; Windsor Castle; Stratfield Saye; The Mill Theatre

For over 150 years The French Horn has served as a charming riverside hotel. Today, it continues that fine tradition of comfortable accommodation, excellent service and gourmet food. Choose to stay in bedrooms or suites located in the hotel or within riverside cottages that are ideally suited for longer stays, and make sure to request a riverside view. The old panelled bar provides an intimate scene for pre-dinner drinks in the award-winning restaurant with whose speciality of locally reared duck is spit roasted on-site over an open fire. The restaurant is a lovely setting for lunch, while at night, diners can enjoy the floodlit view of the graceful weeping willows which fringe the river. Dinner is served by candlelight and the cuisine is a mixture of French and English cooking that uses the freshest ingredients alongside a fine and extensive wine list. This is the perfect location for a romantic getaway, special celebration or corporate event.

Danesfield House Hotel and Spa

HENLEY ROAD, MARLOW-ON-THAMES, BUCKINGHAMSHIRE SL7 2EY
Tel: 01628 891010 **International:** +44 (0)1628 891010
Web: www.condenastjohansens.com/danesfieldhouse **E-mail:** sales@danesfieldhouse.co.uk

Built at the end of the 19th century in an imposing Victorian style, Danesfield House Hotel and Spa is set within 65 acres of stunning gardens overlooking the River Thames with panoramic views across the Chilterns. The executive bedrooms are richly decorated and furnished. Guests may relax in the magnificent Grand Hall, with its minstrels' gallery, in the sun-lit atrium or comfortable bar before taking dinner in one of the 2 restaurants. The Michelin starred restaurant, Adam Simmonds at Danesfield House features the delicious cuisine of chef Adam Simmonds and The Orangery which offers a more traditional menu. Leisure facilities include the award-winning spa with 20-metre ozone-cleansed pool, sauna, steam room, gymnasium and superb treatment rooms. There are also 10 private banqueting and conference rooms. When in London visit Danesfield's award-winning sister spa, Spa Illuminata in Mayfair.

Our inspector loved: *The fabulous Michelin-Starred restaurant and stunning garden views reaching across to the River Thames.*

Price Guide:
single from £134
double/twin from £159
suites from £259

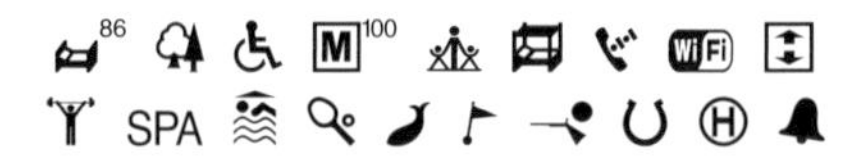

Awards/Recognition: 1 Star Michelin 2012; Condé Nast Johansens Most Excellent Hotel Meeting Venue 2010; Condé Nast Johansens Taittinger Wine List Award, Special Commendation Best Dessert Wine List 2010; 4 AA Rosettes 2012-2013; Voted 12th Top Restaurant in the UK, Good Food Guide 2012

Location: A4155, 0.2 miles; M40 jct 4, 7 miles; Marlow, 3 miles; Heathrow Airport, 23 miles

Attractions: Henley; Windsor; Ascot; River Walks

STOKE PARK

PARK ROAD, STOKE POGES, BUCKINGHAMSHIRE SL2 4PG
Tel: 01753 717171 **International:** +44 (0)1753 717171
Web: www.condenastjohansens.com/stokepark **E-mail:** info@stokepark.com

Our inspector loved: *The grandeur of the Palladian mansion, the luxury and contemporary style of the health pavilion, and the abundance of activities including golf, spa and fine dining.*

Price Guide: (a selection of indulgence breaks is often available)
superior £285
deluxe £335
executive £385
suite £550–£1,500

Awards/Recognition: 2 AA Rosettes 2012-2013

Location: Off the B416; M4 jct 6, 4.5 miles; Windsor, 5 miles; Heathrow Airport, 7 miles

Attractions: Windsor Castle; Ascot; Henley; Legoland

Stoke Park hotel and golf resort offers 5 AA Star luxury accommodation set amidst 350 acres of parkland. For over 900 years it has been at the heart of English heritage, playing host to royalty and aristocracy. The magnificence of the Palladian mansion is echoed in the beautiful interior, enhanced by exquisite antiques, fabrics and paintings. Overlooking breathtaking views, the 49 rooms and suites certainly live up to expectations. All individually furnished, 21 of the bedrooms mirror the hotel's period style, whilst above the £20-million health pavilion, the other 28 resonate luxury modern design. Private bars, cosy lounges, 8 function rooms and the finest restaurants outside London are perfect for entertaining and events. Since 1908 the hotel has been home to one of the world's finest 27-hole championship golf courses. This, along with the spa and health pavilion, truly confirms the hotel's position as one of the country's leading hotel-spa resorts.

The Mere Golf Resort & Spa

CHESTER ROAD, MERE, KNUTSFORD, CHESHIRE WA16 6LJ
Tel: 01565 830155 **International:** +44 (0)1565 830155
Web: www.condenastjohansens.com/themereresort **E-mail:** sales@themereresort.co.uk

A stunning wedding and corporate events venue for 25 years, The Mere is now offering luxury hotel accommodation. Housed in a beautiful red brick Victorian building that dates back to the 12th century, each bedroom and suite features sumptuous king-size beds with fluffy goose down duvets and looks out to beautiful lakeside and garden views. Golf enthusiasts will enjoy the challenging 150-acre, 18-hole championship golf course whilst gourmands will love Browns@TheMere whose menu features a delicious range of classic British flavours accompanied by a comprehensive wine list. It's The Mere's lakeside setting that makes it a wonderfully romantic wedding venue and relaxing setting for The Health Club and Spa where soothing spa treatments and extensive thermal suite facilities including a hammam, caldarium, salt room and hydrotherapy pool are available. After a treatment, savour a light bite to eat or perhaps a glass of Champagne at the Spa Lounge and Bar.

Our inspector loved: *Being pampered in the luxurious spa after a round of golf on the championship course.*

Price Guide:
single from £110
double £120-£200
suite £240-£420

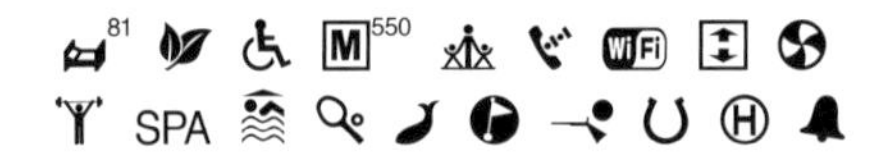

Location: A556, 250yds; M6 jct 19, 2 miles; M56 jct 7, 3 miles; Manchester International Airport, 9.5 miles

Attractions: Liverpool; Tatton Park; Arley Hall and Gardens; Trafford Centre

Carlyon Bay Hotel

SEA ROAD, ST AUSTELL, CORNWALL PL25 3RD
Tel: 01726 812304 **International:** +44 (0)1726 812304
Web: www.condenastjohansens.com/carlyonbay **E-mail:** reservations@carlyonbay.com

Our inspector loved: *Spending the day on the hotel's private beach, then heading back across the golf course for a very civilised afternoon tea.*

Price Guide: (room only)
single £95-£130
double £145-£270
state room £280-£310

Location: A391, 2 miles; St Austell, 3 miles; A30, 13 miles; Newquay Airport, 18 miles

Attractions: The Eden Project; Lost Gardens of Heligan; The Minack Theatre; Fowey

Whether visiting Cornwall on a well-deserved family break or dreaming of a few rounds on a stunning championship golf course, this charming hotel, with its warm Cornish hospitality and truly inspiring location, will certainly exceed all your expectations. From its spectacular vantage point above the cliffs of St Austell Bay featuring idyllic private beaches, take advantage of all the leisure facilities the hotel has to offer, including indoor and outdoor heated pools. Alternatively, simply languish in the luxurious spa - a decadent way to spend the day! The bedrooms have panoramic views of the coastline and are beautifully decorated to imbue a sense of well-being and comfort. The dining venues are as varied as the dishes offered. Within both the Bay View restaurant and the Taste Brasserie the menus showcase the finest locally sourced produce. So relax and let your hosts take care of everything!

THE NARE HOTEL

CARNE BEACH, VERYAN-IN-ROSELAND, TRURO, CORNWALL TR2 5PF
Tel: 01872 501111 **International:** +44 (0)1872 501111
Web: www.condenastjohansens.com/nare **E-mail:** stay@narehotel.co.uk

This absolute gem of a 4-star hotel is superbly positioned overlooking the fine sandy beach of Gerrans Bay. Thanks to Toby Ashworth's proprietorial presence, the hotel has carefully evolved over the years and is considered the most comfortable Cornwall hotel. The winner of Condé Nast Johansens Most Excellent Family Hotel 2011, most bedrooms look out to the sea and have patios and balconies with spectacular views. More sea views are enjoyed from the hotel's 2 restaurants. The main dining room offers a traditional dining experience off the table d'hôte menus where classic English cuisine features local seafood dishes such as Portloe lobster and crab and delicious home-made puddings with generous helpings of Cornish cream. Dinner is also always available in the more informal Quarterdeck Restaurant where al fresco lunches may be taken on the terrace. Explore the glorious Roseland Peninsula's coastline and villages, not forgetting Cornwall's houses and gardens.

Our inspector loved: *The fabulous beach front location, welcoming atmosphere, friendly service and ability to offer something unique and special to all generations.*

Price Guide:
single £140-£268
double/twin £270-£503
suite £334-£768

Awards/Recognition: Condé Nast Johansens Most Excellent Family Hotel 2011; 2 AA Rosette 2012-2013

Location: St Mawes, 8 miles, Truro, 12 miles; St Austell, 12 miles ; A30, 15 miles

Attractions: Eden Project; Lost Gardens of Heligan; Cornish Gardens; National Maritime Museum, Falmouth

THE ROYAL DUCHY HOTEL

CLIFF ROAD, FALMOUTH, CORNWALL TR11 4NX
Tel: 01326 313042 **International:** +44 (0)1326 313042
Web: www.condenastjohansens.com/royalduchy **E-mail:** reservations@royalduchy.com

Our inspector loved: *Relaxing on the sun terrace with a glass of wine and enjoying the wonderful Cornish hospitality.*

Price Guide: (per person)
single £80-£100
double £80-£140
suite £125-£145

43 SPA

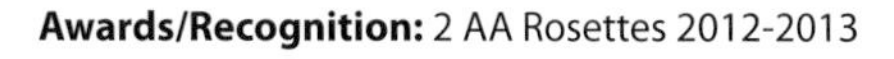

Awards/Recognition: 2 AA Rosettes 2012-2013

Location: A39, 1.8 miles; Falmouth Station, ¾ mile; Penzance, 27 miles

Attractions: National Maritime Museum; Pendennis Castle; The Eden Project; Lost Gardens of Heligan

A popular luxury hotel in the waterside town of Falmouth, The Royal Duchy promises you a relaxing break and the opportunity to get the most out of Cornwall and the West Country. Families are more than welcome, and rooms range from deluxe with sea-front views, to larger interconnecting rooms. Nice touches include binoculars, fresh flowers, slippers and chocolates, and careful consideration is made for those requiring extra beds, cots and bunk beds. Fantastic leisure facilities include an indoor heated pool, snooker room, sauna and treatment room and a full entertainment programme. Dining and drinking options leave you spoilt for choice thanks to the 2 AA Rosette Terrace Restaurant, which presents a wide selection of dishes created from fresh Cornish produce, The Terrace Lounge ideal for lunch with friends, and the chic Terrace Bar where you can enjoy a Duchy cocktail or pint of local beer.

St Michael's Hotel & Spa

GYLLYNGVASE BEACH, FALMOUTH, CORNWALL TR11 4NB
Tel: 01326 312707 **International:** +44 (0)1326 312707
Web: www.condenastjohansens.com/stmichaelsfalmouth **E-mail:** info@stmichaelshotel.co.uk

St Michael's Hotel & Spa, Cornwall, has been carefully and extensively refurbished, resulting in a state-of-the-art health club, spa, award-winning restaurant, and contemporary bedrooms, bars and conference suites. The Flying Fish Restaurant, overlooking the sea and gardens, changes menus regularly so you can sample Cornwall's best fresh fish, seafood and seasonal produce. The sun terrace is the perfect spot for alfresco dining. Surrounded by sub-tropical gardens, the Spa offers an impressive range of health and relaxation treatments, and you can also take a dip in the indoor pool and work out in the large fitness suite. The hotel is ideally located for all the attractions of Falmouth and the nearby area: feel the sand between your toes on the blue flag beach, directly opposite the hotel, or visit the Eden Project within an hour's drive.

Our inspector loved: *The contemporary seaside feel and friendly staff that make this a great hotel for any occasion.*

Price Guide: (per person)
double/twin £59–£105
suite £105–£155

Location: Just off A39; Truro, 11.7 miles; Newquay Airport, 25 miles

Attractions: National Maritime Museum; Land's End; Eden Project; Coastal Walks

Budock Vean - The Hotel on the River

NEAR HELFORD PASSAGE, MAWNAN SMITH, FALMOUTH, CORNWALL TR11 5LG
Tel: 01326 252100 **International:** +44 (0)1326 252100
Web: www.condenastjohansens.com/budockvean **E-mail:** relax@budockvean.co.uk

Our inspector loved: *The great attention to detail, traditional yet friendly service and wealth of facilities in this outstandingly beautiful setting.*

Price Guide: (including dinner)
single £72–£140
double/twin £144–£280
suite £240–£350

Awards/Recognition: 1 AA Rosette 2012–2013

Location: M5 jct 30, 100 miles; A39, 12 miles; Falmouth, 6 miles; Newquay Airport, 30 miles

Attractions: Trebah Gardens; Glendurgan Gardens; National Maritime Museum, Falmouth; Eden Project

This family-run 4-star hotel is set in 65 acres of outstanding natural beauty with award-winning gardens and a private foreshore on the Helford River. One of the country's finest green hotels, Budock Vean is all about relaxation and pampering and has become a destination in itself. Recommended by Condé Nast Johansens since 1983 and current recipient of the Green Tourism Business Scheme Gold Award, guests can enjoy a large indoor pool, outdoor hot tub, sauna, tennis courts, a snooker room, boating, fishing, a Natural Health Spa plus unlimited use of the 9-hole golf course, which was originally designed by James Braid of St Andrews fame. A local ferry will take you from the hotel's jetty to waterside pubs and you can even enjoy a trip on the hotel's own river boat. Imaginative dinners specialise in fresh seafood, which can be walked off on a magnificent myriad of local country and coastal walks.

Rose-In-Vale Country House Hotel

MITHIAN, ST AGNES, CORNWALL TR5 0QD
Tel: 01872 552202 **International:** +44 (0)1872 552202
Web: www.condenastjohansens.com/roseinvalecountryhouse **E-mail:** reception@rose-in-vale-hotel.co.uk

Our inspector loved: *The charming gardens, enticing menus and comfortable rooms.*

Price Guide:
single from £80
double/twin from £135
suite £260

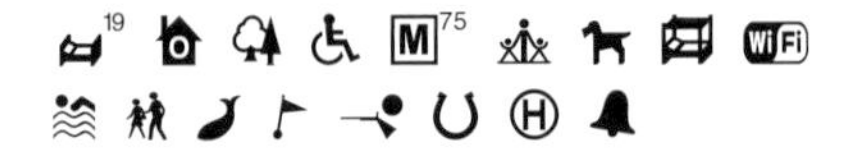

Awards/Recognition: 1 AA Rosette 2012-2013

Location: A3075, 1.4 miles; A30, 2.3 miles; Newquay Airport, 15 miles

Attractions: Local Beaches; Eden Project; Lost Gardens of Heligan; Various National Trust Gardens

A few miles inland from St Agnes you descend into a tranquil wooded valley to discover the 4-star Rose-in-Vale, a welcoming Cornish country house hotel surrounded by charming grounds within a private estate. Owners James and Sara Evans are extremely hospitable and there is a genuine desire to ensure that you have all you need. A light and very spacious dining room is the setting for the carefully thought-out, seasonal menu which features an impressive "surf & turf" option letting you enjoy the best of local meat and freshly caught seafood. Rose-in-Vale provides comfortable bedrooms throughout its picturesque Georgian house including The Rose Suite, which is complete with a four-poster bed, the indulgence of a double Jacuzzi bath and a double 12-jet walk-in shower! Outside, you can relax by the swimming pool, in the hot tub, take your dog for a garden walk or simply find a quiet corner by the duck pond.

Netherwood Hotel

LINDALE ROAD, GRANGE-OVER-SANDS, CUMBRIA LA11 6ET
Tel: 015395 32552 **International:** +44 (0)15395 32552
Web: www.condenastjohansens.com/netherwood **E-mail:** enquiries@netherwood-hotel.co.uk

Our inspector loved: *This imposing family-run hotel with lovely views of Morecambe Bay.*

Price Guide:
single £60-£120
double £95-£200

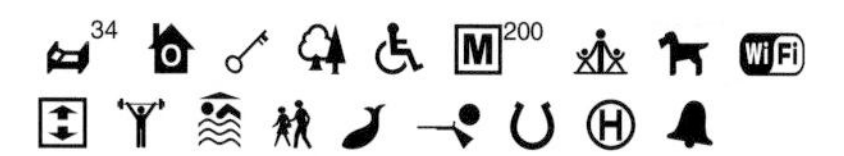

Location: B5277, 500 yards; A590, 3 miles; M6 jct 36, 10 miles; Lake Windermere, 5 miles

Attractions: Lake District National Park; Holker Hall; Levens Hall; Sizergh Castle; Leighton Moss RSPB Reserve

Dramatic and stately in appearance, this friendly hotel - overlooking the wonderful Morecambe Bay - was built as a family house in the 19th century and still exudes a warm, family atmosphere thanks to its longstanding owners, the Fallowfields. Impressive oak panelling is a key feature and provides a fitting backdrop to roaring log fires in the public areas. Bedrooms come with views of the sea, woodlands and gardens. In addition to the main house, Rock House has 4 contemporary bedrooms and The Turrets is a castellated executive self-catering cottage with 2 bedrooms and 2 lounges, ideal for families and groups up to 8. Both are situated a short walking distance away, within the grounds of Netherwood. The restaurant presents local produce and is set on the first floor, which maximises the views over Morecambe Bay. For relaxation there is an indoor pool, spa bath, steam room and fitness centre.

Armathwaite Hall Country House Hotel and Spa

BASSENTHWAITE LAKE, KESWICK, CUMBRIA CA12 4RE
Tel: 017687 76551 **International:** +44 (0)17687 76551
Web: www.condenastjohansens.com/armathwaite **E-mail:** reservations@armathwaite-hall.com

This luxurious 4 AA Red Star hotel in the heart of England's Lake District is set within 400 secluded acres of deer park and woodland. Originally a stately home, its facilities and location are impressive; the perfect place for discovering the nearby Bassenthwaite Lake and Skiddaw Mountain. Full of individuality and character, guest rooms range from the most indulgent Studio Suites to Spa and Club Rooms. Accommodation set within the main house is more traditional in style while the Spa Rooms reflect a contemporary feel. Comfort and relaxation are the essence of Armathwaite Hall, and the award-winning spa with an infinity-edge pool, aroma room, exercise classes and treatment rooms offers an experience or treatment to suit your needs and lifestyle. In addition, the AA Rosette-awarded cuisine, prepared by Master Chef Kevin Dowling, takes advantage of local seasonal produce and Cumbrian specialities to create inspired English and classical French dishes.

Our inspector loved: *The luxurious spa with scenic views from the infinity swimming pool and large outdoor hot tub.*

Price Guide:
single £135
double/twin £200–£330
studio suite £370

Awards/Recognition: 1 AA Rosette 2012-2013

Location: A591, 0.25 miles; A66, 1 mile; M6 jct 40, 25 miles; Keswick, 7 miles

Attractions: Trotters World of Animals; Bassenthwaite Lake; Lake District National Park; Wordsworth and Beatrix Potter Museums

THE LODORE FALLS HOTEL

BORROWDALE, KESWICK, CUMBRIA CA12 5UX
Tel: 017687 77285 **International:** +44 (0)17687 77285
Web: www.condenastjohansens.com/lodorefalls **E-mail:** lodorefalls@lakedistricthotels.net

Our inspector loved: *The panoramic views over Lake Derwentwater from this traditional Lake District family hotel.*

Price Guide:
single £92–£149
double £156–£289
suite £290–£458

Location: B5289, 10yds; A66, 4 miles; M6 jct 40, 22 miles; Keswick, 3.5 miles

Attractions: Derwentwater Launch; Keswick Golf Club; Trotters World of Animals; Honistor Slate Mine with New Via Ferrata Walk/Climb

Close your eyes and imagine stunning lake and mountain views, a waterfall in landscaped gardens, warm hospitality, beauty treatments and an array of leisure facilities as well as good food and service. Open your eyes and see The Lodore Falls, a 4-star hotel in the picturesque Borrowdale Valley. The 69 en-suite Fell Side and Lake View rooms include family rooms and luxurious suites, some with balconies. Light meals and coffee can be enjoyed in the comfortable lounges, whilst the cocktail bar is the ideal venue for a pre-dinner drink. The Lake View restaurant serves the best in English and Continental cuisine accompanied by fine wines. The Beauty Salon, with its 4 treatment rooms, uses the famous Elemis beauty products in its treatments and offers pamper days and luxury days. Family holidays are available including discount vouchers to local attractions.

Dale Head Hall Lakeside Hotel

THIRLMERE, KESWICK, CUMBRIA CA12 4TN
Tel: 017687 72478 **International:** +44 (0)17687 72478
Web: www.condenastjohansens.com/daleheadhall **E-mail:** onthelakeside@daleheadhall.co.uk

The key handed to you upon arrival at Dale Head Hall isn't simply the key to a room – it's the key to complete relaxation. This is the boast of the Hill family, caring owners of this fine hotel that stands alone on the shores of Lake Thirlmere. A bird-watcher's paradise, the setting is nothing less than idyllic, and inside, the furnishings and atmosphere are warm and welcoming. Some of the rooms are located in the Elizabethan house, while others are in the Victorian extension; some have mountain views or stunning lake views as does the lounge. You can enjoy superb food prepared from the finest, freshest seasonal local produce alongside an extensive international wine list in the award-winning lakeside restaurant.

Our inspector loved: *The unrivalled views over Lake Thilmere - this is the only house on the lake.*

Price Guide: (including dinner)
single £130–£160
double £210–£330

Awards/Recognition: 1 AA Rosette 2012-2013

Location: A591, 0.25 miles; M6 jct 40, 14 miles; Keswick, 4 miles; Windermere, 14 miles

Attractions: Dove Cottage and The Wordsworth Museum; Honister Slate Mine; Theatre by the Lake; Rookin House Farm Activity Centre

Gilpin Hotel & Lake House

CROOK ROAD, WINDERMERE, CUMBRIA LA23 3NE
Tel: 015394 88818 **International:** +44 (0)15394 88818
Web: www.condenastjohansens.com/gilpinlodge **E-mail:** hotel@gilpinlodge.co.uk

Our inspector loved: *The luxury and excellent service at this lovely hotel with Lake House located nearby overlooking its own private lake.*

Price Guide: (based on 2 sharing, including 5-course dinner)
single £300-£550
double/twin £320–£420
garden suite £470
lake house suite £500-£600

Awards/Recognition: Relais & Châteaux; 3 AA Rosettes 2012-2013

Location: B5284, 200yds; A591, 6 miles; M6 jct 36, 12 miles; Windermere, 2 miles

Attractions: Windermere; Beatrix Potter Museum; Holker & Levens Halls; Blackwell Arts and Crafts House

A luxury Lake District Hotel, Gilpin Hotel has been family run for 25 years, and as well as having won a multitude of awards it is well loved by those who visit for special breaks and romantic weekends or simply as a haven to unwind. The service is warm and personal yet relaxed, and every room is designed and furnished with huge attention to detail. Many have patio doors leading out onto the beautiful gardens, with spa baths or hot tubs, and in 2010 the family was proud to present the opening of the Gilpin Lake House. Simply stunning, it is located one mile from the Hotel and is set in 100 acres of grounds on the shore of a private lake - known as Knipe Tarn - with boat house and jetty and a spa for exclusive use of Lake House guests. All of the individually created suites make the most of their beautiful setting, and each evening a chauffeur will take you to and from the Hotel's AA 3 Rosette-awarded restaurant for dinner.

Holbeck Ghyll Country House Hotel

HOLBECK LANE, WINDERMERE, CUMBRIA LA23 1LU
Tel: 01539 432 375 **International:** +44 (0)1539 432 375
Web: www.condenastjohansens.com/holbeckghyll **E-mail:** stay@holbeckghyll.com

Our inspector loved: *The delicious dinner in the oak-panelled restaurant with panoramic views over Lake Windermere.*

Price Guide: (including 4-course dinner)
single from £230
double/twin £290–£360
suite £400–£450

Awards/Recognition: 1 Star Michelin 2012; 3 AA Rosettes 2012-2013

Location: A591, 0.5 mile; M6 jct 36, 20 miles; Windermere, 3 miles; Ambleside, 1 mile

Attractions: Lake Windermere; Lake District National Park; Dove Cottage & Rydal Mount; Brockhole Visitors Centre

Boasting breathtaking views over Lake Windermere and the Lakeland Fells, Holbeck Ghyll is nestled amidst acres of natural beauty. Built in the 19th century, the traditional Arts & Crafts style remains to this day, apparent in the wealth of detail throughout the house including stained-glass windows and carved wooden panelling. Renowned for its restaurant's fine cuisine, which has held a Michelin Star for 12 consecutive years and presents an award-winning wine list, the hotel also offers luxurious accommodation, a health spa and superb service, which includes a concierge facility that can arrange activities from helicopter flights to super car hire. In addition, there is a variety of accommodation to choose from such as deluxe en-suite rooms in the main house, contemporary lodge rooms within the grounds, the exclusive Miss Potter Suite, ideal for special celebrations, and self-contained cottages with private garden and hot tub.

LINTHWAITE HOUSE

CROOK ROAD, WINDERMERE, CUMBRIA LA23 3JA
Tel: 015394 88600 **International:** +44 (0)15394 88600
Web: www.condenastjohansens.com/linthwaitehouse **E-mail:** stay@linthwaite.com

Our inspector loved: *The friendly atmosphere of this elegant hotel with stunning views overlooking Lake Windermere.*

Price Guide:
single £171-£244
double £204-£344
suite £283-£554

Awards/Recognition: Condé Nast Johansens and Champagne Taittinger Wine List Awards, Wine List of the Year 2011

Location: B5284, 0.25 miles; Windermere, 2 miles; A591, 2 miles; M6 Jct 36, 14 miles

Attractions: Windermere; Beatrix Potter Museums & Dove Cottage; Lake District National Park

Linthwaite House is located at the heart of England within the Lake District, amidst 14 acres of garden and woodland overlooking Lake Windermere and Belle Isle. The hotel combines stylish originality and luxury accommodation with the best of traditional hospitality. Most bedrooms have lake, garden or fell views. Linthwaite's newest room is the luxurious Luxury Lake View room with outdoor 'Hot Tub'. The restaurant offers excellent cuisine with the best of fresh, local produce accompanied by a fine selection of wines. There is a 9 hole putting green within the grounds and a par 3 practice hole. You can if you wish, fish for brown trout in the hotel tarn. Fell walks begin at the front door, and you can follow in the footsteps of Wordsworth and Beatrix Potter to explore the spectacular scenery.

LAKESIDE HOTEL & SPA ON LAKE WINDERMERE

LAKESIDE, NEWBY BRIDGE, CUMBRIA LA12 8AT
Tel: 015395 30001 **International:** +44 (0)15395 30001
Web: www.condenastjohansens.com/lakeside **E-mail:** sales@Lakesidehotel.co.uk

A picturesque and unique location on the edge of Lake Windermere, this classic, relaxed and traditional 4-star hotel will have cast its spell on you by the time your visit is over. Many bedrooms have breathtaking lake vistas, and menus in both the award-winning Lakeview Restaurant or Ruskin's Brasserie include Cumbrian favourites. To get a real Lake's experience there are cruisers berthed adjacent to the hotel ready for further exploration and adventure. For inclement weather the Pool and Spa, exclusively available for hotel residents, comprises of a 17m indoor pool, gym, sauna, steam room and Aveda treatment rooms. For business guests, the exclusive Business and Events Centre, Windermere Suite, is located opposite the hotel. Available for private use, it offers delegates the best of both worlds: discreet privacy and 4-star hotel splendour.

Our inspector loved: *Taking a swim in the pool and relaxing with a massage in the spa before enjoying morning coffee in the Lakeside Conservatory.*

Price Guide:
single from £140
double/twin £165–£340
suite from £280

Awards/Recognition: Condé Nast Johanens Most Excellent Waterside Hotel Award 2009; 2 AA Rosettes 2012-2013

Location: A590, 1 mile; M6 jct 36, 15 miles; Newby Bridge, 1 mile

Attractions: Windermere Lake Cruisers and Aquarium of the Lakes; Lakeland Motor Museum; Lakeside and Haverthwaite Steam Railway; Holker Hall and Gardens

Fischer's Baslow Hall

CALVER ROAD, BASLOW, DERBYSHIRE DE45 1RR
Tel: 01246 583259 **International:** +44 (0)1246 583259
Web: www.condenastjohansens.com/fischers **E-mail:** reservations@fischers-baslowhall.co.uk

Our inspector loved: *The beautiful and lovingly tended flower and kitchen gardens where the hotel's chefs collect fruit, vegetables and herbs for use in their dishes.*

Price Guide:
single £105–£150
double/twin £155–£240

Awards/Recognition: 1 Star Michelin 2012; 4 AA Rosettes 2010–2011

Location: A623, 50yds; Bakewell, 4 miles; M1 Jct 29, 40-min drive; Manchester Airport, 1-hour drive

Attractions: Chatsworth; Haddon Hall; Market Towns of Bakewell and Buxton; Peak District National Park

Within walking distance of the Chatsworth Estate, this is the perfect base for exploring the Peak District. Reached via a tree-lined drive, Baslow Hall has all the glorious trademarks of a 17th-century manor house, however the Hall was built in 1907 and remains a beloved family home. Owners Max and Susan Fischer bought the property in 1988 and filled it with their own furniture and art collection to create a personal feel. 11 bedrooms are individually styled with the emphasis on comfort; 6 traditional rooms are located in the Main House and 5 more contemporarily designed rooms are situated in the adjacent Garden Rooms. Food is an important part of Baslow Hall, with Head Chef Rupert Rowley's cooking constantly evolving. Heavily relying on British produce he fuses modern and classic dishes. Executive Chef Max, who has held a Michelin Star since 1994, tends a much admired garden that provides fruit, vegetables and herbs for the kitchen.

GIDLEIGH PARK

CHAGFORD, DEVON TQ13 8HH
Tel: 01647 432367 **International:** +44 (0)1647 432367
Web: www.condenastjohansens.com/gidleighpark **E-mail:** gidleighpark@gidleigh.co.uk

Situated in the heart of Dartmoor National Park you will appreciate the family-run Gidleigh Park for its outstanding international reputation for comfort and gastronomy. A clutch of top culinary awards including 2 Michelin Stars for its imaginative cuisine and the wine list, make it one of the best in Britain. Service throughout the hotel is faultless. The bedrooms – 2 of which are located in a converted chapel – are furnished with original antiques. The public rooms are well-appointed and during the cooler months, a fire burns in the lounge's impressive fireplace. Privacy is complete, amidst 107 secluded acres in the Teign Valley. A croquet lawn and a splendid water garden can be found in the grounds. A 360-yard long, par 52 putting course designed by Peter Alliss opened in 1995.

Our inspector loved: *The fabulous food, fine wines and beautiful bedrooms make this a very special place to stay.*

Price Guide:
room/suite £325 – £1175

24 M 20 WiFi

Awards/Recognition: Condé Nast Johansens Taittinger Wine List Award, Best Champagne List 2012; Condé Nast Johansens Most Excellent Restaurant 2011; Voted Number One in the Sunday Times Top 100 Restaurants 2011; 4 AA Rosettes 2012-2013; 2 Star Michelin 2012; Relais & Châteaux

Location: A382, 2.5 miles; A30, 4.79 miles; M5 jct 31, 20 miles; Exeter St. Davids Railway Station, 21 miles; Exeter International Airport, 28.5 miles

Attractions: Castle Drogo; Dartmouth; Exeter Cathedral; Dartmoor National Park; RHS Rosemoor

COMBE HOUSE

GITTISHAM, NEAR HONITON, EXETER, DEVON EX14 3AD
Tel: 01404 540400 **International:** +44 (0)1404 540400
Web: www.condenastjohansens.com/combehousegittisham **E-mail:** stay@combehousedevon.com

Our inspector loved: *The fabulous home-grown cuisine and relaxed atmosphere that make this magical country house a perfect retreat close to the sea and pretty countryside.*

Price Guide:
single from £190
double/twin from £215
suite from £375

Awards/Recognition: Condé Nast Johansens Most Romantic Hotel 2012 and Most Excellent Country House Hotel 2010

Location: M5 jct 29/A303/A30 and Honiton/Fenny Bridges, 15-min drive; Exeter Airport, 12-min drive; Train Station, 8-min drive (Honiton/London Waterloo)

Attractions: South West Coast, Sidmouth to Lyme Regis; Cathedral City of Exeter; Honiton Antique Shops and Galleries, Dartmoor

Ken and Ruth Hunt have enjoyed 14 years at the helm of this elegant 16th-century Elizabethan manor set in beautiful gardens and 3,500 acres of some of England's finest countryside, resulting in a very special retreat that continues to find new ways to delight. Voted in the Top 3 Best Foodie Hotels in the South West, this hidden away hotel and restaurant with restored Victorian kitchen gardens is simply magical. Bedrooms and suites provide a stunning combination of contemporary, comfortable furnishings, fine antiques and fresh flowers. A romantic thatch cottage for 2 with huge walled garden is tucked away within the estate. The 2 Master Chefs of GB love to use Combe's own produce and this year there is the addition of egg laying chickens in the woodland gardens. Well chosen wines and warm, genuine hospitality are always on the menu here, located a short drive to the South West Coast, Sidmouth to Lyme Regis and wide open spaces of Dartmoor.

The Tides Reach Hotel

SOUTH SANDS, SALCOMBE, DEVON TQ8 8LJ
Tel: 01548 843466 **International:** +44 (0)1548 843466
Web: www.condenastjohansens.com/tidesreach **E-mail:** enquire@tidesreach.com

This south-facing charming hotel sits in a sandy cove just inside the mouth of the Salcombe Estuary. Family run for over 42 years, the Edwards family have gained a reputation for warmth, hospitality and excellent service. Chef Finn Ibsen creates menus with seasonal produce and makes the most of the morning catch from the local fishermen. Most of the immaculate bedrooms come with lovely sea views and offer plenty of flexibility for families. There's an indoor pool, sauna, spa, snooker table and for the very energetic, a squash court. Sailing fans may wish to hire a Hobie Cat and sail into Salcombe for an ice-cream or spot of shopping and then happily retreat from the hordes to the comfort of Tides Reach.

Our inspector loved: *The exceptional service and beautiful coastal setting.*

Price Guide: (including dinner)
single £78–£190
double/twin £146–£380

Awards/Recognition: 1 AA Rosette 2012-2013

Location: A381, 2 miles; M5, 43 miles; Salcombe, 1.7 miles; Exeter Airport, 45 miles

Attractions: Gardens of Overbecks; Plymouth Maritime Museum; South Devon Coastal Path; Dartmoor

Hotel Riviera

THE ESPLANADE, SIDMOUTH, DEVON EX10 8AY
Tel: 01395 515201 **International:** +44 (0)1395 515201
Web: www.condenastjohansens.com/riviera **E-mail:** enquiries@hotelriviera.co.uk

Our inspector loved: *The traditional and welcoming atmosphere and well-appointed rooms at this great British classic on Sidmouth's esplanade.*

Price Guide: (including 6-course dinner)
single £130–£194
double/twin £260–£368
suite £400–£420

Awards/Recognition: 1 AA Rosette 2012-2013

Location: A3052, 2.5 miles; M5 jct 30, 13 miles; Exeter Airport, 10 miles; Honiton/Exeter St Davids Railway Stations, 8/15 miles

Attractions: Killerton House and Gardens; Exeter Cathedral; Powderham Castle; Dartmoor

This most prestigious, award-winning and welcoming sea view hotel is located in Lyme Bay. Peter Wharton's Hotel Riviera is arguably one of the most comfortable and most hospitable in the region offering fine dining, a fantastic wine cellar and excellent service. The exterior, with its fine Regency façade and bow-fronted windows, complements the elegance of the interior comprising handsome public rooms and beautifully appointed bedrooms, many with sea views. Perfectly located at the centre of Sidmouth's historic Georgian esplanade, and awarded 4 Stars by both the AA and Visit Britain, the Riviera is committed to providing the very highest standards of excellence. Choose to dine in the attractive salon, with panoramic views across Lyme Bay, and indulge in the superb cuisine, prepared by English and French trained chefs. The exceptional cellar will please any wine connoisseur. Festive programmes and short breaks are available.

Watersmeet Hotel

MORTEHOE, WOOLACOMBE, DEVON EX34 7EB
Tel: 01271 870333 **International:** +44 (0)1271 870333
Web: www.condenastjohansens.com/watersmeet **E-mail:** info@watersmeethotel.co.uk

From its elevated position at the water's edge of Combesgate Beach, Watersmeet overlooks incomparable natural beauty from one of the finest and most dramatic locations in the South West. The breathtaking views of the ever-changing, rugged coastline over to Lundy Island can be admired from large picture windows in the reception rooms. And due to a refurbishment, many of the guest rooms now have balconies with sea views, and of course, all the accruements for luxury living. Take lunch and tea al fresco on the terrace or in the tea garden and dine by candlelight while watching the sunset at the pavilion restaurant. The award-winning cuisine is well-balanced, imaginative and features local ingredients. Recreational facilities include a heated outdoor pool, indoor pool with hot spa, a steam room, coastal walks along National Trust land, Saunton Sands Championship Golf Course and the sandy beach below reached via steps directly from the hotel.

Our inspector loved: *The beautiful location, fantastic views and traditional hospitality make this a favourite place to return to time and again.*

Price Guide: (including dinner)
single £98–£150
double/twin £150–£340
suite £220–£360

Awards/Recognition: 1 AA Rosette 2012-2013

Location: B3343, 2 miles; A361, 4 miles; M5 jct 27, 50 miles; Barnstaple, 15 miles

Attractions: National Trust Coastal Walks; Arlington Court; Saunton Sands Champion Golf Course; Watermouth Castle

Captains Club Hotel & Spa

WICK FERRY, WICK LANE, CHRISTCHURCH, DORSET BH23 1HU
Tel: 01202 475111 **International:** +44 (0)1202 475111
Web: www.condenastjohansens.com/captainsclubhotel **E-mail:** enquiries@captainsclubhotel.com

Our inspector loved: *The fabulous waterfront location and bright spacious bedrooms.*

Price Guide: (room only)
single £179
double £179-£249
suite/apartment £299-£699

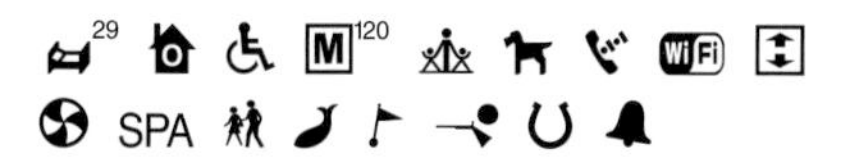

Awards/Recognition: 2 AA Rosettes 2012-2013

Location: A35, 5 min-drive; Christchurch Railway Station, 1 mile; Bournemouth, 6 miles; Bournemouth International Airport, 15 min-drive

Attractions: Christchurch Priory; Christchurch Harbour; River and Sea Cruise; New Forest National Park

Sleek, smooth and ultra modern, Captain's Club Hotel is a testament to designer flair. This strikingly contemporary luxury boutique 4-star hotel resides on the banks of the River Stour, an interesting short walk from Christchurch. Among the multitude of offerings, enjoy soothing spa treatments, trips across the bay aboard the hotel's 34-foot luxury motor cruiser, strolling along the quayside to the historic town's priory church - which boasts choir stalls older than those in Westminster Abbey - and sitting back in a so-comfortable armchair to absorb superb vistas through floor-to-ceiling windows. Each bedroom and suite has been decorated in a maritime theme, features cutting-edge amenities and looks out to a stunning riverside view. The restaurant's cuisine reflects the feel of the hotel: uncomplicated, fresh, innovative and ultimately satisfying. The afternoon tea platter is a must!

Christchurch Harbour Hotel & Spa

95 MUDEFORD, CHRISTCHURCH, DORSET BH23 3NT
Tel: 01202 483434 **International:** +44 (0)1202 483434
Web: www.condenastjohansens.com/christchurchharbour **E-mail:** christchurch@harbourhotels.co.uk

Our inspector loved: *The wonderful views and friendly service at this very comfortable hotel.*

Price Guide: (including dinner)
single £125-£185
double £145-£230

Awards/Recognition: 2 AA Rosettes 2012-2013

Location: Avon Beach, 0.5 miles; Bournemouth, 10 miles; Southampton, 25 miles; London, 80 miles

Attractions: New Forest; Isle of Wight; Hengistbury Head; Avon Beach

Close to the world famous Dorset Heritage Coast, Bournemouth and New Forest National Park, Christchurch Harbour Hotel & Spa provides luxury accommodation, with many rooms and public spaces boasting picturesque views across Mudeford Quay towards Hengistbury Head. While sophisticated, the hotel is relaxed, and with its purposefully designed spa on-site to nourish your body and soul, you will have no choice but to indulge and unwind. Bedrooms vary in shape and size and all are tastefully decorated in a contemporary style complete with facilities such as WiFi, flat-screen TVs and iPod docking stations. With the beach just a walk away, this is an ideal location for wonderful family holidays. Dining here is a treat – not only can you eat by the waterside at the Harbour Restaurant and Terrace but a wander into the grounds will lead you to the jetty, an informal relaxed restaurant headed up by Alex Aitkin.

Summer Lodge Country House Hotel, Restaurant and Spa

9 FORE STREET, EVERSHOT, DORSET DT2 0JR
Tel: 01935 482000 **International:** +44 (0)1935 482000 **U.S. Toll Free:** 1 877 955 1515
Web: www.condenastjohansens.com/summerlodge **E-mail:** summerlodge@rchmail.com

***Our inspector loved:** Everything from the fabulous afternoon teas to the superb cuisine and luxurious bedrooms and spa.*

Price Guide:
double from £210
suite from £340

Awards/Recognition: Condé Nast Johansens Most Outstanding Service 2010; Relais & Châteaux; 3 AA Rosettes 2012-2013

Location: A37, 1.5 miles; M5 jct 25, 33.5 miles; Dorchester, 13 miles; Bournemouth, 46 miles

Attractions: Thomas Hardy Country; Cerne Abbas; Abbotsbury and Heritage Coast; Sherborne and Shaftesbury

Summer Lodge is the ultimate escape to the English countryside, nestled in 4 acres of breathtaking gardens in the heart of Wessex. Built in 1798 for the second Earl of Ilchester, it was then renovated by local architect and novelist Thomas Hardy, and was a private residence for over 200 years. A proud member of Relais & Châteaux, it offers a relaxing ambience, courtesy, comfort, exceptional cuisine and service, and feels more like a home than a hotel. The bedrooms, suites and cottages are tastefully decorated and combine the finest English furnishings with the latest technology, including free WiFi. The award-winning restaurant, under Head Chef Steven Titman and world-renowned Sommelier Eric Zwiebel, serves delicious cuisine, using the abundant fresh local produce and the hotel's own herb garden; the traditional Dorset cream teas are legendary. There is also a magnificent conservatory-style pool, health spa and gym, a croquet lawn and bicycles.

DORSET - LYME REGIS

Alexandra Hotel and Restaurant

POUND STREET, LYME REGIS, DORSET DT7 3HZ
Tel: 01297 442010 **International:** +44 (0)1297 442010
Web: www.condenastjohansens.com/hotelalexandra **E-mail:** enquiries@hotelalexandra.co.uk

Set in an elevated position close to the centre of Lyme Regis, this welcoming family-run hotel enjoys a sensational sea view of Lyme Bay and the famous Cobb Harbour. Dating from the 18th century, the "Alex" was once the home of the Dowager Countess Poulett and later Duc de Stacpoole, and has been a hotel since the 1900s. History and tradition are an integral part of its very English charm, and a recent refurbishment has injected a fresh, contemporary look to the lounge, reception areas, and the majority of the guest rooms, many of which overlook the sea beyond pretty lawned gardens. Enjoy the coastal views, among the best in the country, from a fabulous new deck area, the perfect spot for a light lunch, Dorset cream tea or pre-dinner cocktail. There are 2 restaurants: the sunny Conservatory and the more formal Alexandra. Both capitalise on the region's fresh, local produce. A perfect base for exploring the beaches and dramatic scenery of the Jurassic Coast.

Our inspector loved: *The contemporary styling of the bedrooms, fabulous views and superb cream teas.*

Price Guide:
single from £85
double £177-£255

Awards/Recognition: Condé Nast Johansens Most Excellent Waterside Hotel 2011; Taste of the West Silver Award 2011

Location: On the A3052; A35, 3 miles; Honiton, 11 miles

Attractions: South West Coast Path; Part of UNESCO World Heritage Site; Fossil Walks; Marine Aquarium; Seaton Tramway

Rockliffe Hall Hotel, Golf & Spa

HURWORTH-ON-TEES, NEAR DARLINGTON, DURHAM DL2 2DU
Tel: 01325 729999 **International:** +44 (0)1325 729999
Web: www.condenastjohansens.com/rockliffehall **E-mail:** enquiries@rockliffehall.com

Our inspector loved: *Never wanting to leave this luxurious resort with its excellent spa and delicious food.*

Price Guide:
single £175-£295
double £210-£495
suite £375-£530

Awards/Recognition: Condé Nast Johansens and Corinthia Hotels Most Excellent MICE Awards, Venues that Accommodate Groups of Under 100, 2011; 3 AA Rosettes 2012-2013

Location: A167, 1 mile; A1(M), 5 miles; Darlington, 5 miles; Durham Tees Valley Airport, 6 miles; Newcastle International Airport, 46 miles

Attractions: North East Coast; Newcastle-upon-Tyne; Yorkshire Dales; York and Durham

Set amidst 375 acres of beautiful North Yorkshire countryside, and with its own championship golf course on the doorstep, this 5-star luxury hotel was built as a private mansion in 1863 and is now at the centre of one of the finest resort destinations in the North of England. The Hall's history can be glimpsed in numerous period details and original features, such as carved stone pillars, oak balustrades and ornate ceilings. As befits a resort with such a contemporary, elegant and relaxed ambience, service and attention to detail are simply outstanding, as is Michelin-Starred Chef Kenny Atkinson's refined, modern British cuisine. One of the largest in the country, the hotel's stunning spa offers an impressive array of pampering treatments and activities in the state-of-the-art technogym and kinesis studio.

Bibury Court

BIBURY, GLOUCESTERSHIRE GL7 5NT
Tel: 01285 740337 **International:** +44 (0)1285 740337
Web: www.condenastjohansens.com/biburycourt **E-mail:** hello@biburycourt.com

Our inspector loved: *Some of the gorgeous new rooms and bathrooms such as the Pepys and the East India Company.*

Price Guide: (including Continental breakfast)
single £95
double from £105
suite £345

Awards/Recognition: 2 AA Rosettes 2012-2013

Location: Just off B4425; A40, 8.5 miles; Cirencester, 7 miles; Cheltenham, 22 miles

Attractions: Stow-on-the-Wold; Bourton-on-the-Water; Arlington Row; Hidcote Manor Gardens

Bibury Court is a stunning Jacobean mansion located in the beautiful Cotswold village of Bibury. Focusing on good food and fine wines, the hotel uses the best of local produce in its menus, ranging from light lunchtime dishes to haute cuisine at dinner. Whether for business or pleasure, it is the perfect location and setting for a romantic weekend, family holiday or business function. The interior is an eclectic mix of traditional grandeur mixed with new cutting-edge design. All 18 bedrooms are unique, many with four-poster beds, and for those who really want a treat, there is the very spacious King James I Suite, complete with a wet room shower and marble infinity bath. The hotel's 6 acres of stunning landscaped grounds are the ideal setting for any outdoor event or wedding. Guests can take afternoon tea in the secluded areas of the garden, walk through the orchard or indulge in a spot of fishing on the River Coln.

Cotswold House Hotel & Spa

HIGH STREET, CHIPPING CAMPDEN, GLOUCESTERSHIRE GL55 6AN

Tel: 01386 840330 **International:** +44 (0)1386 840330

Web: www.condenastjohansens.com/cotswoldhouse **E-mail:** reservations@cotswoldhouse.com

Our inspector loved: *The fabulous spa and excellent village location. This is the perfect place for a weekend of pampering and exploring The Cotswolds.*

Price Guide:
single from £120
double/twin from £140
suite from £240

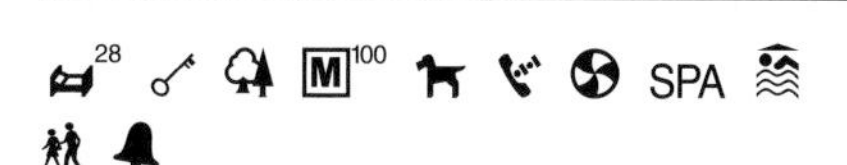

Location: B4081, 0.25 miles; A44, 2 miles; M5 jct 8, 25 miles

Attractions: Shopping in Chipping Campden; Stratford-upon-Avon; Oxford; The Cotswolds

Cotswold House is a privately owned boutique hotel in a beautiful Regency town house in the heart of Chipping Campden. Expect a warm welcome, tranquillity and contemporary comfort whether your stay is for a special event, family break or romantic getaway. Each bedroom, suite and cottage is a peaceful retreat decorated in warm tones fitted with state-of-the-art technology and delightfully sumptuous bathrooms. Original artwork adorns the walls and modern glass sculptures, and award-winning lighting enhance the property's stylish individuality and inviting ambience. Unwind and enjoy all-day dining where the finest seasonal produce is always on the menu and using locally sourced ingredients whenever possible. Complete your visit with a trip to the Spa, located within the former coach house, for a range of holistic and results-driven treatments including massages, facials and aromatherapy.

Barnsley House

BARNSLEY, CIRENCESTER, GLOUCESTERSHIRE GL7 5EE
Tel: 01285 740000 **International:** +44 (0)1285 740000
Web: www.condenastjohansens.com/barnsleyhouse **E-mail:** info@barnsleyhouse.com

Surrounded by enchanting gardens and ancient meadows, this charming Cotswolds hotel has a style of its own. Built as a private house in the 17th century by the local squire, it is now a stylish, character-filled country home that you can comfortably retreat to for a tranquil break or invigorating spa weekend. The superb gardens and grounds attract thousands of paying visitors but they do not encroach on the privacy and required standards for you as a hotel guest. The focus at Barnsley House is on comfort, luxury, service, good food and wine in congenial surroundings. Traditional stone fireplaces, wood floors and heavy beams merge with contemporary furnishings and 21st-century facilities. Bedrooms are a testament to modern design, the cuisine is sumptuous and a big screen cinema room is available for you to sit back and view films at selected times.

Our inspector loved: *The private cinema with its pink leather seats, the intimate spa and wonderful atmosphere.*

Price Guide:
superior £275-£325
stableyard suite £385-£440
deluxe garden suite £495-£545

Location: M4 jct15, 25-min drive; Bibury, 8-min drive; Cirencester, 10-min drive; Kemble Railway Station, 15-min drive; Bristol Airport, 90-min drive

Attractions: Bibury Village; Cirencester; Cheltenham

Burleigh Court

BURLEIGH, MINCHINHAMPTON, NEAR STROUD, GLOUCESTERSHIRE GL5 2PF
Tel: 01453 883804 **International:** +44 (0)1453 883804
Web: www.condenastjohansens.com/burleighgloucestershire **E-mail:** burleighcourt@aol.com

Our inspector loved: *The attention to detail, home-from-home atmosphere and elevated views across the open countryside.*

Price Guide:
single £90-£110
double £140-£160
suite £200

Awards/Recognition: 2 AA Rosettes 2012-2013

Location: A419, 0.5 miles; M4 jct, 28.5 miles; Cirencester, 11.5 miles; Cheltenham, 16 miles

Attractions: Cotswolds; Bath; Slimbridge Wildfowl Trust; Westonbirt Arboretum

Journey through honey-stoned Cotswold villages to reach this 18th-century former gentleman's manor that is now a charming hotel. Nestling on a steep hillside overlooking the Golden Valley its relaxed atmosphere and acres of beautifully tended gardens featuring terraces, ponds, pools, hidden pathways and Cotswold stone walls create an idyllic setting. Many bedrooms in the main house have garden views, though for families Condé Nast Johansens recommends the coach house rooms located by a Victorian plunge pool or those within the courtyard gardens which offer flexible accommodation. The restaurant has a reputation for classical dishes and a wine cellar to satisfy the most discerning drinker. From here you can easily explore the market towns of Minchinhampton, Tetbury, Cirencester, Painswick and Bibury.

The Manor House Hotel

MORETON-IN-MARSH, GLOUCESTERSHIRE GL56 0LJ
Tel: 01608 650501 **International:** +44 (0)1608 650501
Web: www.condenastjohansens.com/manorhousemoreton **E-mail:** info@manorhousehotel.info

Dating back to the 16th century, this enchanting 4-star hotel in the heart of England is steeped in a fine history that is reflected in its décor, its sensitive refurbishment and exceptional hospitality. On entering you cannot help but be impressed by the effortless combination of plush fabrics, elegant furnishings and practical contemporary convenience. The atmosphere is informal and friendly, where nothing is too much trouble. If it's a nice day take a stroll through the secluded garden filled with sweet scented flowers and meandering pathways to discover a 300-year-old mulberry tree and mature evergreen oak, or soak up the warmth on the sun terrace - the perfect place for an evening cocktail. The award-winning restaurant is a special treat where most of the produce is local with seasonal twists that remind you of your countryside location. The hotel is also ideal for small board meetings for up to 10 and can host up to 120 for presentations and conferences.

Our inspector loved: *The stylish bar combined with the light and airy restaurant, cosy bedrooms and fabulous location.*

Price Guide:
double/twin £158-£260
suite £220-£350

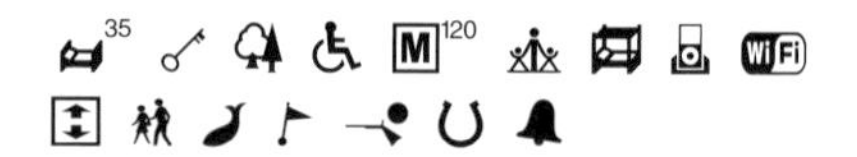

Awards/Recognition: 2 AA Rosettes 2012-2013

Location: On the A429; M40, jct 8/15, 22 miles; Cheltenham, 20 miles; Birmingham International Airport, 40 miles

Attractions: Cheltenham Races, Bath and Oxford; Stratford-upon-Avon; Blenheim Palace; Westonbirt Concerts and Events

Calcot Manor Hotel & Spa

NEAR TETBURY, GLOUCESTERSHIRE GL8 8YJ
Tel: 01666 890391 **International:** +44 (0)1666 890391
Web: www.condenastjohansens.com/calcotmanor **E-mail:** reception@calcotmanor.co.uk

Our inspector loved: *The comprehensive facilities and understated luxury that make this the perfect stay for any occasion.*

Price Guide:
double/twin £275-£355
family room £295-£410
family suite £380-£460

Awards/Recognition: Condé Nast Johansens Most Excellent Family Friendly Hotel 2010 and 2012; 2 AA Rosettes 2012-2013

Location: On the A4135; Tetbury, 3.5 miles; M5 jct 13, 11 miles; M4 jct 18, 12.5 miles

Attractions: Westonbirt Arboretum; Bath; Cotswolds; Cirencester

Calcot Manor is an enchanting Cotswolds hotel set in over 200 acres of meadowland. Dating back to the 14th century, it boasts 700 years of history; the original building was erected in 1300AD! Further to a sensitive refurbishment, it is now a luxurious haven offering extensive facilities and spacious, individually and tastefully designed bedrooms with every modern comfort. Calcot also has a crèche and wonderful facilities for families, including dedicated family rooms and suites. Enjoy gourmet dishes at the Conservatory Restaurant whilst gazing over delightful countryside views. However, if you're in the mood for traditional pub meals, then the exceptional Gumstool Inn is for you; its wonderful sun terrace is the perfect spot for al fresco dining. Be sure to visit the spa, a welcome retreat providing a wide range of therapies as well as a gymnasium, hot tub and pool.

Heckfield Place

HECKFIELD, HAMPSHIRE RG27 0LD
Tel: 0118 932 6868 **International:** +44 (0)118 932 6868
Web: www.condenastjohansens.com/heckfieldplace **E-mail:** reservations@heckfieldplace.com

Our inspector loved: *The attention to detail in the renovation of this fine country house, and the extensive grounds that include a working farm.*

Price Guide: (including breakfast, tax and service charges)
superior from £400
deluxe from £600
suite £800-£5000

Location: M4 jct 11, 6 miles; Reading Train Station, 10 miles; Heathrow, 32 miles; A33 Swallowfield Bypass, 2 miles

Attractions: Stratfield Saye House; West Green House; Jane Austen's House Museum; Highclere Castle

Due to open in March 2013 Heckfield Place sits in the heart of the rolling Hampshire countryside with dramatic views over gardens, lakes, woods and farmland. This 200-year old country house has the feel of a private home, full of warmth and whimsy. The rich interiors are English and eclectic with contemporary tweeds nudging up against classic pewter and cutting-edge technology nestled amongst the antiques. With 60 individually designed rooms, suites and cottages there is a wonderful choice of accommodation and guests can enjoy a variety of experiences from literary salons to music recitals, foraging weekends, wine tastings and viewings in the 60-seat underground cinema. Heckfield Place is not just a country house hotel but a 400-acre estate where rare-breed livestock are raised and classic British vegetables are grown. Skye Gyngell is the Culinary Director and her distinctive philosophy informs every aspect of dining from sourcing ingredients through to presentation.

Lime Wood

BEAULIEU ROAD, LYNDHURST, HAMPSHIRE SO43 7FZ
Tel: 023 8028 7177 **International:** +44 (0)23 8028 7177
Web: www.condenastjohansens.com/limewood **E-mail:** info@limewood.co.uk

Our inspector loved: *The stunning bedrooms, unpretentious Scullery restaurant and the sheer indulgence of the luxury spa.*

Price Guide:
eaves/cosy £245-£345
spacious/generous £345-£445
forest suite £445-£775

Awards/Recognition: Condé Nast Johansens Most Excellent Country House Hotel 2012; Relais & Châteaux; 3 AA Rosettes 2012-2013

Location: A31, 0.5 miles; Lyndhurst, 1.5 miles; London, 90-min drive; Southampton, 12 miles

Attractions: New Forest National Park; Highcliffe Beach; Motor Museum, Beaulieu; Lymington; Foraging

Set in the heart of the New Forest, and within easy driving distance from London, this child-friendly 5-star luxury hotel is the perfect destination for a weekend getaway or family break. Built as a hunting lodge in the 17th century, this luxurious Regency-style country house hotel was recently renovated with a fresh approach, reviving its original architecture and grounds yet keeping its charm and character. The generously sized bedrooms and suites are filled with indulgent touches, antiques and hand-picked pieces of art; some have a log fire or wood-burning stove. Activities include foraging, forest walks and bike rides, and for relaxation there is the state-of-the-art Herb House Spa offering a variety of holistic and Ayurvedic spa treatments. Head Chef Luke Holder creates imaginative hearty British fare based on local organic produce, served in the glamorous Dining Room or the more informal setting of the Scullery.

Chewton Glen

NEW FOREST, HAMPSHIRE BH25 6QS
Tel: 01425 275341 **International:** +44 (0)1425 275341 **US Toll Free:** 1 800 344 5087
Web: www.condenastjohansens.com/chewtonglen **E-mail:** reservations@chewtonglen.com

Our inspector loved: *The new Tree House Suites.*

Price Guide:
bronze from £280
suite from £580

Awards/Recognition: Condé Nast Johansens Most Excellent Hotel 2012; Relais & Châteaux

Location: Heathrow, 85 miles; M27 jct 1, 14 miles; Southampton Airport, 26 miles; Mainline Train Station, 2 miles

Attractions: New Forest National Park; Isle of Wight; Bournemouth; Lymington

Arrive with exceptional expectations and you certainly won't be disappointed. Chewton Glen is set in 130 acres of gardens and parkland on the edge of the New Forest, not far from the sea. Each bedroom and suite is the ultimate in luxury with marble bathrooms, cosy bathrobes and views over the grounds. And now recently opened Tree House Suites offer alternative accommodation set in a wooded valley within the hotel grounds. Set on stilts, these eco-conscious suites are very romantic, complete with kitchenettes. Try Vetiver, the new dining experience where Executive Chef Luke Matthews creates surprising and innovative dishes from fresh local produce alongside an impressive wine list. And allow yourself to be seduced by the stunning spa with its magnificent 17-metre swimming pool, steam, sauna, treatment rooms, gym and hydrotherapy pool. Outside there's another pool, sun terrace, croquet lawn, tennis and a 9-hole par 3 course.

Tylney Hall

ROTHERWICK, HOOK, HAMPSHIRE RG27 9AZ
Tel: 01256 764881 **International:** +44 (0)1256 764881
Web: www.condenastjohansens.com/tylneyhall **E-mail:** reservations@tylneyhall.com

Our inspector loved: *Taking afternoon tea in the magnificent Italian lounge whilst marvelling at the opulent surroundings.*

Price Guide:
double/twin £220–£360
suite £430–£500

Awards/Recognition: 2 AA Rosettes 2012-2013

Location: A30, 1 mile; M3 jct 5, 3 miles; Basingstoke, 6.5 miles; Heathrow, 32 miles

Attractions: Watercress Line Steam Railway; Historic Cathedral City of Winchester; West Green House and Gardens; Jane Austen's House

Arriving at Tylney Hall in the evening, with its floodlit forecourt fountain, it is easy to imagine attending a private party in a stately home. Set in 66 acres of ornamental gardens and parkland, this impressive Grade II listed mansion typifies the great houses of another era. The bedrooms are luxuriously appointed; some have four-poster beds and spa baths. Food plays a big part here; guests can enjoy exquisite meals in the award-winning Oak Room Restaurant or on the terrace during summer. Surrounding the hotel are beautiful wooded trails ideal for jogging, a lake with boathouse bridge, an orchard and Victorian greenhouses. The leisure facilities include 2 swimming pools, all-weather tennis courts, croquet, snooker and mountain bike hire, whilst golf is available at the adjacent 18-hole golf course. The health spa offers 5 treatment rooms, a gym, saunas and whirlpool. Weddings, conferences and special events can be held in the 12 private banqueting rooms.

CASTLE HOUSE

CASTLE STREET, HEREFORD, HEREFORDSHIRE HR1 2NW
Tel: 01432 356321 **International:** +44 (0)1432 356321
Web: www.condenastjohansens.com/castlehse **E-mail:** info@castlehse.co.uk

Our inspector loved: *This elegant town house hotel with luxurious bedrooms and peaceful location overlooking the Castle Moat.*

Price Guide:
single from £110
double from £150
suite £195–£230

Awards/Recognition: 2 AA Rosettes 2012-2013

Location: Centre of Hereford; Off the A438; A49, 0.8 miles; M4 jct 20, 43 miles

Attractions: Mappa Mundi and Chained Library at Hereford Cathedral; Ludlow; Hay on Wye; Cheltenham

Located in the heart of the city, just 100m from Hereford Cathedral, this town house hotel with Rosette-awarded restaurant is a testament to luxury boutique style. Step though the door of the immaculate Georgian façade to a warm welcome and bright lobby area dominated by a grand staircase before being led to your comfortable bedroom within the main hotel or at nearby "Number 25" Castle Street. The Restaurant, overseen by Head Chef Claire Nicholls, serves English dishes with an international twist prepared from locally sourced produce and home-grown vegetables. In fact, most of the menu's beef and lamb have been reared on the owner's nearby farm. Especially good is the fillet of beef with sweet potato dauphinoise, caramelised shallots and wild mushroom compote. The Castle Bar and Bistro is ideal for lighter lunches and snacks. A beautifully landscaped garden runs down to the old castle moat and is perfect for enjoying

SOPWELL HOUSE

COTTONMILL LANE, SOPWELL, ST ALBANS, HERTFORDSHIRE AL1 2HQ
Tel: 01727 864477 **International:** +44 (0)1727 864477
Web: www.condenastjohansens.com/sopwellhouse **E-mail:** enquiries@sopwellhouse.co.uk

Our inspector loved: *The affordable spa break packages.*

Price Guide:
single £109
double/twin £124
suite from £164

Location: St Albans Station, 6-min drive; Luton Airport, 20-min drive; M1 jct 8/M25 jct 22, 8-min drive; A1M jct 3, 10-min drive

Attractions: St Albans Cathedral; Willows Farm Village & Park; Butterfly World Project; Warner Bros. Studio Tour London – The Making of Harry Potter

Formerly Lord Mountbatten's country home, Sopwell House is now a stylish 12-acre retreat and sought-after venue for weddings, special events and business meetings. Furthermore, it is a premier leisure break destination with a luxurious newly refurbished day spa, extensive Country Club and par 72 golf course on its doorstep. There is also a fine dining restaurant offering a contemporary British menu created by Paris-trained Executive Chef James Chapman and the recently renovated Brasserie serving simple, flavoursome classics and worldwide-inspired dishes. The Cocktail Bar and Lounge is popular for informal gatherings whilst The Terrace Lounge, filled with light and looking out to garden views, is the ideal spot for afternoon tea. Maintaining the traditional ambience of its Georgian heritage, each bedroom, suite and apartment has every modern comfort; stay in a spacious Mews Apartment set apart from the main hotel, for a particularly private stay.

THE GEORGE OF STAMFORD

ST MARTINS, STAMFORD, LINCOLNSHIRE PE9 2LB
Tel: 01780 750750 **International:** +44 (0)1780 750750
Web: www.condenastjohansens.com/georgeofstamford **E-mail:** reservations@georgehotelofstamford.com

Our inspector loved: *Dining al fresco in the courtyard and an award-winning wine list at this wonderful coaching inn that is run with passion and enthusiasm.*

Price Guide:
single from £95
double from £150
superior from £230

Awards/Recognition: Condé Nast Johansens Champagne Taittinger Wine List Award, Overall Winner 2012; Condé Nast Johansens Taittinger Wine List Award, Special Commendation Staff Training 2010; 1 AA Rosette 2012–2013

Location: Town Centre; A1, 1 mile; Peterborough, 10 miles; London, 1-hour train ride

Attractions: The Architectural Gem of Stamford; Burghley House; Rutland Water; Market Towns of Oakham and Uppingham

As you drive along one of the most famous highways in the world, you are sure to see the "Gallows" sign for this traditional English coaching inn, a delightful hotel with over 900 years of fascinating history. A popular meeting point for the locals of Stamford and an idyllic weekend getaway destination, this is one of England's great architectural gems and purveyor of great food. The cuisine is superb, the wines are first class, and the surroundings are charming and time-honoured; a wonderful silver carving trolley is used and reminiscent of bygone days. During the warmer months, you can enjoy a meal in the courtyard. Bedrooms are very individual, some with beams or oak panelling and others in bold designer fabrics. The devotion to good hospitality is evident in every member of the team who work at this friendly, bustling hotel.

41

41 BUCKINGHAM PALACE ROAD, LONDON SW1W 0PS
Tel: 020 7300 0041 **International:** +44 (0)20 7300 0041 **US Toll Free:** 1 877 955 1515
Web: www.condenastjohansens.com/41buckinghampalaceroad **E-mail:** book41@rchmail.com

Our inspector loved: *The emphasis on service and hospitality at this little gem!*

Price Guide:
king from £329
suite from £353
master suite from £869

Awards/Recognition: Condé Nast Johansens Most Excellent London Hotel 2011

Location: Victoria Station, 5-min walk; St Pancras/Eurostar, 3.6 miles; Heathrow Airport, 15 miles; Gatwick Airport, 23 miles; Stansted Airport, 37 miles

Attractions: Buckingham Palace; London Eye; Houses of Parliament; Hyde Park

This boutique hotel of splendid luxury overlooks the Royal Mews and is consistently rated as TripAdvisor's No 1 London Hotel. Within a 5-minute walk of Buckingham Palace and Victoria Station, this exclusive little gem is renowned for its exceptional value, caring service, generous hospitality and thoughtful touches. Beyond the striking architecture is a black and white themed interior design where distinguishing features and services such as a choice of turndown options, an honesty bar and 24-hour informal dining, make guests feel truly at home; there is even a pantry filled with tasty home-made treats for a midnight feast! Bedrooms and suites are furnished in hand carved mahogany and black leather, feature iPod docking stations, movies, music, free WiFi and extravagantly comfortable hand stitched English mattresses. Next door is the cosy Leopard Bar, the more traditional Library Restaurant and bbar for exotic cocktails and South African fusion cuisine.

Cheval Phoenix House

1 WILBRAHAM PLACE, SLOANE STREET, LONDON, SW1X 9AE
Tel: 020 7259 8222 **International:** +44 (0)20 7259 8222
Web: www.condenastjohansens.com/phoenixhouse **E-mail:** cph@chevalresidences.com

The award-winning, charming Cheval Phoenix House is nestled in the heart of Chelsea. A private residence with attentive 24-hour concierge service, it is an exclusive gateway to one of London's most desirable neighbourhoods, just minutes from the boutiques and galleries of Sloane Square, close to Duke of York Square and designer shops at Chelsea Harbour. After a long day of Chelsea living indulge in opulent organic hampers, pamper yourself with Aveda toiletries and rest in sumptuous beds fitted with fine Frette linens. Each residence is a stylish setting for entertaining but if you'd rather dine out, the innovative Le Cercle restaurant is on the doorstep. Try the superb French grazing menu or enlist the skill of a Le Cercle chef in the privacy of your residence. Available as studios, 1 or 2-bedroom apartments and duplexes, Cheval Phoenix House offers a variety of accommodation to suit a range of requirements, for short breaks or longer stays.

Our inspector loved: *The duplex with sophisticated minimalism.*

Price Guide: (per night, excluding VAT, minimum 7-day stay. Full terms and conditions available.)
studio from £200
1-bedroom apartment from £260
1-bedroom duplex from £357
2-bedroom apartment from £383
2 x 1 interconnecting duplex from £786

Location: Sloane Square Tube Station, 5-min walk

Attractions: Royal Court Theatre; Sloane Square; Saatchi Gallery; Le Cercle Restaurant

The Wyndham Grand London Chelsea Harbour

CHELSEA HARBOUR, LONDON SW10 0XG
Tel: 020 7823 3000 **International:** +44 (0)20 7823 3000
Web: www.condenastjohansens.com/wyndhamlondon **E-mail:** wyndhamlondon@wyndham.com

Our inspector loved: *The location, superb facilities and dining in the award-winning restaurant.*

Price Guide:
suite from £220
penthouse from £1,500

Awards/Recognition: 1 AA Rosette 2012–2013

Location: Imperial Wharf Railway Station, 5-min walk; London St Pancras, 7 miles; London Heathrow Airport, 14 miles

Attractions: Chelsea Harbour Design Centre; Harrods; Harvey Nichols; King's Road; Westfield Shopping Centre

A unique hotel for London, The Wyndham Grand is an impressive 5-star, all-suite property that sits proudly overlooking the boats moored in exclusive Chelsea Harbour. Its West London location is ideal for a break exploring all the central London sites and shopping on the King's Road and Sloane Street. The suites are spacious, immaculate and the detail reflects thoughtful consideration for the seasoned traveller, alternatively you can enjoy elevated luxury in the Penthouses with panoramic views and unique art. There is something incredibly relaxing about dining at the award-winning restauraunt Chelsea Riverside Brasserie, where you can eat outside on warm days. You get a feeling that you are anywhere other than a city centre, yet a short ride in the river launch will take city travellers right to the centre of the Docklands, whilst the more fashion conscious will enjoy the chauffeur service to the heart of Knightsbridge.

CHEVAL CALICO HOUSE

42 BOW LANE, LONDON EC4M 9DT
Tel: 020 7489 2500 **International:** +44 (0)20 7489 2500
Web: www.condenastjohansens.com/calicohouse **E-mail:** cch@chevalresidences.com

The City is the beating heart of London, home to St Paul's Cathedral, the Tate Modern, Bank of England and the Barbican arts complex. Located just off Bow Lane is the exclusive Cheval Calico House comprising elegant 1 and 2-bedroom apartments. Equally ideal as a base for business and pleasure, the apartments are available for both short and extended stays. Guests enjoy the freedom of a private residence whilst benefiting from the convenience and facilities of a hotel. Air-cooling, WiFi, Bose Soundlink, Samsung Smart TVs, 24-hour concierge, on-site management and a daily maid service ensure that your stay is a memorable and enjoyable one.

Our inspector loved: *Rubbing shoulders with historic London.*

Price Guide: (per night, excluding VAT, minimum 7-day stay. Full terms and conditions available.)
open plan 1-bedroom apartment from £156
1-bedroom apartment from £163
2-bedroom apartment from £211
2-bedroom penthouse from £267

Location: Mansion House Tube Station, 5-min walk; London City Airport, 7 miles; Heathrow Airport, 18 miles; Eurostar St Pancras, 2 miles

Attractions: St Paul's Cathedral; Tower of London; Borough Market; Shopping

THE MAYFLOWER HOTEL

26-28 TREBOVIR ROAD, LONDON SW5 9NJ
Tel: 020 7370 0991 **International:** +44 (0)20 7370 0991
Web: www.condenastjohansens.com/mayflower **E-mail:** info@mayflower-group.co.uk

Our inspector loved: *The cool Colonial reception and juice bar.*

Price Guide:
double £120-£155
suite £130-£195

 48 M 25   

Awards/Recognition: 4 AA Rosettes 2012-2013

Location: Earls Court Underground Station, 2-min walk; M4 jct1, 8 miles; Heathrow Airport, 14 miles; Waterloo International, 5 miles

Attractions: Buckingham Palace; Harrods; Victoria and Albert Museum; Hyde Park

Great value for money, The Mayflower town house hotel is a wonderful example of Eastern influences in the centre of London. Full of originality, this is the perfect haven if you're travelling alone or on business. The guest rooms on the ground floor are small yet stylish and rich in pale stone, vibrant fabrics and Indian and Oriental antiques, however, Johansens guests preferring more space should ask for one of the first floor bedrooms - refurbished in light, fresh colours with sparkling glass lighting and mirrors. Stylish bathrooms sparkle with slate and chrome and have walk-in showers. A Continental buffet breakfast is served in the downstairs dining room, or when the weather is fine, in the extended patio garden. You can grab a caffeine or vitamin C fix in the coffee and juice bar before heading out to Knightsbridge, Chelsea and surrounding attractions such as the Natural History and Science Museums. The hotel is close to the Earls Court Exhibition Centre.

LONDON - EARLS COURT

Twenty Nevern Square

20 NEVERN SQUARE, LONDON SW5 9PD
Tel: 020 7565 9555 **International:** +44 (0)20 7565 9555
Web: www.condenastjohansens.com/twentynevernsquare **E-mail:** hotel@twentynevernsquare.co.uk

Our inspector loved: *The discreet location opposite a quiet leafy square yet so close to central London!*

Price Guide:
double/twin £130–£165
suite £275

Location: Earls Court Underground, 2-min walk; M4, 8 miles; Heathrow Airport, 14 miles; Gatwick Airport, 35 miles

Attractions: Victoria and Albert Museum; Natural History Museum; Harrods; Hyde Park

This wonderful town house hotel is located close to Earls Court and Olympia Exhibition Centres, and is just 10 minutes from designer shops, restaurants, theatres and attractions such as the Victoria and Albert Musuem and the Science Museum. An elegant 4-star hotel, Twenty Nevern Square provides a unique hospitality experience. Its sumptuously restored, compact bedrooms emphasise natural materials, hand-carved beds and white marble. Choose from the delicate silks of the Chinese Room or touch of opulence in the Rococo Room. If you're looking to really spoil someone, then the grandeur and style of the new Ottoman Suite is the perfect treat! Breakfast is served in the light, bright Conservatory opening onto a decked balcony area, and gym facilities are available by arrangement.

Corinthia Hotel London

WHITEHALL PLACE, LONDON, SW1A 2BD
Tel: 020 7321 3000 **International:** +44 (0)20 7321 3000
Web: www.condenastjohansens.com/corinthialondon **E-mail:** reservations.london@corinthia.com

Our inspector loved: *The "wow" factor at every turn, the design, comfort, service and incredible spa!*

Price Guide:
single from £309
double from £369
suite from £599

Location: Heathrow Airport, 1-hour drive; St Pancras International Station, 30-min drive; Charing Cross Tube Station, 5-min walk; Embankment Tube Station, 5-min walk

Attractions: Trafalgar Square; National Gallery; Thames Embankment; West End Theatres

The prime, central location of Corinthia Hotel London is just one of its many outstanding highlights. Creatively designed guest rooms, suites and penthouses, 3 first-class dining options, 4 enticing bars and the largest luxury spa in the capital complete this 5-star picture. Trafalgar Square, Westminster and Covent Garden are within walking distance; Mayfair and the City's Square Mile are close by. However, it's tempting to spend a day at ESPA Life at Corinthia comprising 17 treatment pods, a Daniel Galvin hair salon, make over room, indoor pool and Private Spa Suite. Alternatively, experience afternoon tea in The Lobby Lounge, where the services of a tea sommelier enhance this truly British experience. Other gastronomic delights include fine Mediterranean dining at Massimo Restaurant & Oyster Bar and superb British fare at the modern Northall, whilst the hotel's bars offer additional menus, sharing dishes, a charcuterie, selected Champagnes and bespoke cocktails.

130 Queen's Gate Apartments

130 QUEEN'S GATE, KENSINGTON, LONDON SW7 5LE
Tel: 0207 9385930 **International:** +44 (0)207 9385930
Web: www.condenastjohansens.com/queensgate **E-mail:** reservations@maykenbel.co.uk

Our inspector loved: *The generous room dimensions and contemporary décor in addition to the convenient location for exploring London.*

Price Guide: (apartment per night, excluding VAT)
1-bedroom from £316
2-bedroom from £412
3-bedroom from £542
penthouse prices upon request

Location: South Kensington Tube Station, 5-min walk; Gloucester Road Tube Station, 10-min walk; Heathrow Airport, 40-min drive

Attractions: High Street Kensington; Museums in Exhibition Road; Royal Albert Hall; Hyde Park

In the heart of London's royal borough of Kensington and Chelsea, this Neoclassical-style property originally stood as 4 stylish 19th-century town houses. Today it comprises 50 freshly refurbished luxury apartments. Fully serviced, they range from 4-bedroomed penthouses through to studio apartments. While each accommodation retains period features they offer an uncluttered, contemporary feel for those who may be travelling alone, as a couple or with their family. Spacious and light, they are immaculately fitted with state-of-the-art equipment, wooden flooring and premium finishing touches. Furnishings can be provided on a flexible basis to suit guests' specific needs. Staffed around the clock by professional multi-lingual staff, services include everything you would expect from a 5-star hotel, from general housekeeping to making reservations and booking appointments. A personal chef can also be arranged.

Cheval Gloucester Park

ASHBURN PLACE, KENSINGTON, LONDON SW7 4LL
Tel: 020 7373 1444 **International:** +44 (0)20 7373 1444
Web: www.condenastjohansens.com/gloucesterpark **E-mail:** cgp@chevalresidences.com

Our inspector loved: *The Champagne welcome hamper for longer stays.*

Price Guide: (per night, excluding VAT, minimum 7-day stay. Full terms and conditions available.)
1-bedroom apartment from £238
2-bedroom apartment from £300
3-bedroom apartment from £525

Location: Gloucester Road Tube Station, 1-min walk; High Street Kensington Tube Station, 10-min walk

Attractions: Royal Albert Hall; Kensington Gardens; National History Museum; Shopping; Restaurants

Perfectly located in the heart of London, the unique Cheval Gloucester Park is just a short stroll from Kensington Gardens and Knightsbridge, convenient for exploring the boutiques of Kensington, Harvey Nichols, Harrods and Hyde Park. Comfortable and spacious, each 1, 2 and 3-bedroom apartment is available for bookings of 7 days or longer. They are intelligently designed, impeccably furnished and feature a sense of playful fun; most boast unparalleled views across London. A knowledgeable 24-hour concierge is at your disposal to help with any arrangements or reservations and a daily housekeeping service from Mondays through to Fridays maintains impeccable standards. Designed for luxury living, treat Cheval Goucester Park as your very own London home.

Cheval Thorney Court

PALACE GATE, KENSINGTON, LONDON W8 5NJ
Tel: 020 7581 5324 **International:** +44 (0)20 7581 5324
Web: www.condenastjohansens.com/thorneycourt **E-mail:** ctc@chevalresidences.com

Cheval Thorney Court effortlessly combines tradition, privacy and security. Just minutes from parks and gardens, palaces and museums, this is one of Kensington's most desirable addresses. Most of the penthouses and apartments overlook Kensington Gardens and each is furnished with a distinctly timeless Georgian elegance, Regency stripes, leather-topped writing bureaus, marble bathrooms, sumptuous dining rooms and an overall stately home ambience. Cheval Thorney Court is the perfect destination for those seeking upscale accommodation for an extended stay and a sumptuous setting for entertaining in style. The concierge desk is attended 24-hours a day and a daily maid service is in operation Mondays-Fridays.

***Our inspector loved:** The wonderfully surprising spacious "country house" feel.*

Price Guide: (excluding VAT, minimum 22-day stay. Full terms and conditions available.)
2-bedroom apartment from £336
2-bedroom penthouse from £600
3-bedroom apartment from £625

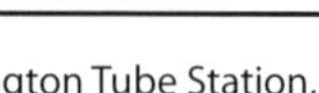

Location: High Street Kensington Tube Station, 10-min walk; Gloucester Road Tube Station, 10-min walk

Attractions: Royal Albert Hall; Kensington Gardens; Shopping; Museums

THE MILESTONE HOTEL

1 KENSINGTON COURT, LONDON W8 5DL
Tel: 020 7917 1000 **International:** +44 (0)20 7917 1000 **U.S. Toll Free:** 1 877 955 1515
Web: www.condenastjohansens.com/milestone **E-mail:** bookms@rchmail.com

Our inspector loved: *The style of this award-winning hotel with imaginatively decorated suites. Pure romantics should ask for the "Mistinguette Suite" complete with private terrace!*

Price Guide:
king from £354
suite from £737
apartment from £629 (7-night minimum stay)

Awards/Recognition: Voted No 1 Hotel in London "Best Places to Stay" Condé Nast Traveler Gold List 2011; 2 AA Rosettes 2012-2013

Location: Kensington High Street, 5-min walk; Paddington Heathrow Express, 2.18 miles; Heathrow Airport, 13.6 miles; Gatwick Airport, 37 miles

Attractions: Kensington Palace and Gardens; Royal Albert Hall; Buckingham Palace; Harrods; The Natural History Museum

The 5-star luxury Milestone Hotel, overlooking Kensington Gardens, is in the heart of London's most exclusive shopping district, a short walk from popular museums and only a few minutes' taxi ride from the West End. An architectural and historical treasure, its blend of personal service, splendidly luxurious accommodation and inspired cuisine has won many awards including No. 1 London Hotel on the Condé Nast Traveller Gold List 2011. Each guest room is different, dressed with fine fabrics, fresh flowers, antique furnishings and rare works of art. The club-like panelled bar is cosy and the chic black and white conservatory is ideal for intimate meetings, teas or light snacks. Sophisticated Cheneston's Restaurant serves some of the finest cuisine in the city. And the fitness centre, with resistance pool, sauna and therapy treatments, allows you to stay in shape and get pampered. The Milestone is famous for its philosophy of "no request is too large, no detail too small."

The Adria

88 QUEEN'S GATE, LONDON SW7 5AB
Tel: 020 7118 8988 **International:** +44 (0)20 7118 8988
Web: www.condenastjohansens.com/theadria **E-mail:** stay@theadria.com

Our inspector loved: *The welcoming atmosphere, beautiful décor and excellent location of this wonderful new boutique hotel.*

Price Guide: (including Continental breakfast)
deluxe from £250
executive from £310
suite from £400

Location: South Kensington Underground Train Station, 4-min walk; Heathrow, 14 miles; Gatwick, 35 miles

Attractions: Hyde Park; Natural History Museum; Harrods; King's Road, Chelsea

For a hotel whose mission is to create a home-away-from-home, The Adria does not disappoint. Lovingly transformed from a Victorian town house into a chic, comfortable boutique residence, its interior design mix of the contemporary and traditional perfectly complements the elegant spaces and lofty ceilings. Upon arrival a Butler greets you with a welcome drink, then following check-in in the Drawing Room you will be shown to your room. Each of the 22 rooms and 2 suites reflects a traditional British theme, and no expense has been spared on the gorgeous furnishings, luxurious marble bathrooms and sumptuous linens. The hotel offers a bespoke dining service, however, The Morning Room presents delicious breakfasts each day, including an Arabic favourite, Foul Mesdames. While alcohol is not served, you are just a stone's throw from the King's Road with its restaurants and bars, in addition to Chelsea's fabulous shopping.

Beaufort House

45 BEAUFORT GARDENS, KNIGHTSBRIDGE, LONDON SW3 1PN
Tel: 020 7584 2600 **International:** +44 (0)20 7584 2600
Web: www.condenastjohansens.com/beauforthouseapartments **E-mail:** info@beauforthouse.co.uk

Our inspector loved: *The dedicated, attentive staff who ensure that every home comfort is available.*

Price Guide: (excluding VAT)
£245–£900

 21      

Location: Knightsbridge Underground, 3-min walk; Victoria Station, 2 miles; Heathrow, 14 miles; Gatwick, 28 miles

Attractions: Harrods; Hyde Park; Buckingham Palace; Victoria and Albert Museum

Beaufort House resides on a tranquil and exclusive tree-lined Regency cul-de-sac offering 21 self-contained luxury serviced apartments, ranging from an intimate 1-bedroom to a spacious 4-bedroom apartment. Light, fresh, modish interiors are decorated in neutral tones complemented by stylish accents of colour. Kitchens are bright, crisp white spaces; very conducive to culinary creativity! Ideal for families, guests enjoy each apartment's seclusion and comfortable atmosphere of a private home with the benefits of a first-class hotel. All apartments have direct dial telephones with voice mail, safes, iPod connectors and wireless internet; some benefit from balconies or patios. The apartments are serviced daily at no additional charge and full laundry/dry cleaning services are available. The 24-hour Guests Services team is happy to organise theatre tickets, restaurant bookings and a chauffeur. Beaufort House was awarded Enjoy England's Gold Award 2012.

Cheval Knightsbridge

15 CHEVAL PLACE, LONDON, SW7 1EW
Tel: 020 7225 3325 **International:** +44 (0)20 7225 3325
Web: www.condenastjohansens.com/chevalknightsbridge **E-mail:** ck@chevalresidences.com

Our inspector loved: *The choice of locations.*

Price Guide: (per night, excluding VAT, minimum 7-day stay. Full terms and conditions available.)
2-bedroom apartment from £336
2-bedroom mews/town house from £393
3-bedroom apartment from £529
3-bedroom town house from £508
3-bedroom cottage from £500 (min 3-month stay)

Location: Knightsbridge Tube Station, 3-min walk; South Kensington Tube Station, 7-min walk

Attractions: Harrods; Victoria and Albert Museum; Shopping; Restaurants

Peacefully located in an exclusive and desirable Knightsbridge neighbourhood, close to the Victoria and Albert Museum, Harvey Nichols, Hyde Park and Harrods, is Cheval Knightsbridge residences. Comprising mews houses, apartments, town houses and a city cottage, guests experience the best of both worlds: the comforts of a private home coupled with the service expected from the finest hotel. Consider your chosen residence your London home; each designed with an individual style and character that can be perfectly matched to your tastes and requirements. Created for extended stays, every residence includes all your essential creature comforts such as a beautiful kitchen and the latest communication technology. A dedicated team of attentive staff is on-hand to look after every detail of your stay, leaving you free to explore your surroundings and fully immerse yourself into London life.

Claverley Court

BEAUFORT GARDENS, LONDON SW3 1PS
Tel: 020 7938 5930 **International:** +44 (0)20 7938 5930
Web: www.condenastjohansens.com/claverleycourt **E-mail:** reservations@maykenbel.co.uk

Our inspector loved: *The contemporary comfort and smart London address.*

Price Guide: (apartment per night)
studio apartment from £180
1-bedroom apartment from £320
2-bedroom apartment from £510
3-bedroom suite on request

Location: Knightsbridge Underground Tube Station, 5-min walk; Heathrow Airport, 40-min drive

Attractions: Knightsbridge High End Shopping; Hyde Park; Victoria and Albert Museum; Restaurants

Just around the corner from Harrods, this stylishly converted London town house offers a range of luxuriously furnished studio, 1, 2 and 3-bedroom apartments. Painstakingly planned by an in-house team who have engaged the help of Italian carpenters and design houses, the décor will satisfy the most discerning of visitors. The top-floor penthouse and family suites feature exotic Madagascar marble and walnut floors, and all are adorned with fine fabrics, elegant wallpapers and Wilton carpets creating a contemporary, comfortable feel. Natural light is maximised and enhanced by low intensity, environmentally-friendly lighting systems throughout. Daily housekeeping and a discreet service ensure that - even for an extended stay - the apartments will feel like a home-from-home. Surrounding Claverley Court's quiet, residential street is Knightsbridge and all it has to offer, from the numerous restaurants, shops, antique and art dealers, to chic bars and night clubs.

The Egerton House Hotel

17-19 EGERTON TERRACE, KNIGHTSBRIDGE, LONDON SW3 2BX
Tel: 020 7589 2412 **International:** +44 (0)20 7589 2412 **US Toll Free:** 1 877 955 1515
Web: www.condenastjohansens.com/egertonhouse **E-mail:** bookeg@rchmail.com

The exclusive Egerton House is perfectly situated on a secluded residential street in Knightsbridge, just a 3-minute walk from Harrods, close to the Victoria and Albert Museum, Sloane Street and Central London's attractions. This enchanting Victorian house offers the ultimate "feel at home" experience with caring staff, thoughtful signature touches and splendid luxury. Each room and suite has its own character and design ranging from lavish traditional to striking contemporary and is adorned with exquisite furnishings, antiques and artworks that include Picasso, Braque and Matisse, all complemented by modern amenities such as flat-screen TVs, free WiFi and specially programmed video iPods. Delicious breakfasts, high teas and daily specials are prepared from the freshest produce and served in the charmingly sophisticated restaurant or in the cosy, elegant lounge and bar. For martini lovers, Head Barman Antonio Pizzuto is renowned for serving London's finest.

Our inspector loved: *The fact that discerning guests travel across oceans to stay here, and of course, Antonio's magical martinis.*

Price Guide:
double from £330
studio from £636
Victoria & Albert suite from £1,104

Awards/Recognition: Condé Nast Johansens Most Excellent City Hotel 2012

Location: Knightsbridge Underground, 5-min walk; Victoria Station, 2 miles; Heathrow, 14 miles; Gatwick, 28 miles

Attractions: Harrods; Victoria and Albert Museum; Hyde Park; Buckingham Palace

THE ARCH LONDON

50, GREAT CUMBERLAND PLACE, MARBLE ARCH, LONDON W1H 7FD
Tel: 020 7724 4700 **International:** +44 (0)20 7724 4700
Web: www.condenastjohansens.com/thearchlondon **E-mail:** info@thearchlondon.com

Our inspector loved: *The sleek, bold style with clever contemporary features, and the professional service.*

Price Guide: (excluding VAT)
single from £185
double from £220
suite from £415

Location: Marble Arch Tube Station, 2-min walk; Heathrow Express/Paddington Station, 5-min drive; Heathrow Airport, 40-min drive

Attractions: Selfridges; Hyde Park; Marylebone High Street/Shopping Boutiques; Oxford Street/ Bond Street Shopping

Offering "London lifestyle at its best," this sleek, contemporary boutique hotel is located on a quiet residential street close to London's Marble Arch and Bond Street. The property comprises 82 guest rooms and suites, each decorated in a bespoke colour scheme designed to reflect the character of the building and its surroundings, and features a luxurious bathroom, state-of-the-art technology, vibrant art, crisp linens and sumptuous textiles and furnishings. Special touches include black granite and mirrored finishes, in-bath TVs, rain showers, widescreen TVs and exclusive Malin + Goetz products. Visitors looking for the perfect mix of glamour and hospitality won't be disappointed by The Bar's cocktail menu, the sophistication of Le Salon de Champagne and the open kitchen of the lively HUNter 486 Brasserie, named after the 1950s district dialling code for Marylebone.

The Mandeville Hotel

MANDEVILLE PLACE, LONDON W1U 2BE
Tel: 020 7935 5599 **International:** +44 20 7935 5599
Web: www.condenastjohansens.com/mandeville **E-mail:** sales@mandeville.co.uk

The Mandeville is an exciting and opulent central London hotel offering a very personalised service based on a "nothing is too much trouble" philosophy. Style and sophistication is paramount here, from the town house apartment-style terrace suite with its indulgent bathroom, to decadent features and lighting in the lobby. In fact, each bedroom is exquisitely furnished with fabrics of striking textures and tones from some of the leading London design houses. Breakfast, Sunday brunch, lunch, afternoon tea and dinner are all served at Reform Social and Grill, an informal yet sophisticated restaurant serving an extensive British-inspired menu prepared to an exceptionally high standard. Be sure to peruse the cocktail list featuring British classics made with some of the finest spirits distilled in the UK. And book the Red Room for your next meeting or private party; it is the perfect location, just minutes from Oxford Street, Bond Street and Mayfair.

Our inspector loved: *The attention to detail, superb service and central location.*

Price Guide: (room only, excluding VAT)
single from £250
superior from £270
deluxe from £290

Location: Bond Street Underground, 0.2 miles; Heathrow Airport, 15 miles; Victoria Station, 2 miles

Attractions: The Wallace Collection; Selfridges; Wigmore Hall; The Regent's Park; Hyde Park

The May Fair

STRATTON STREET, MAYFAIR, LONDON W1J 8LT
Tel: 020 7769 4041 **International:** +44 (0)20 7769 4041
Web: www.condenastjohansens.com/mayfair **E-mail:** sales@themayfairhotel.co.uk

Our inspector loved: *The Schiaparelli Suite filled with Buddhist attributes, and Silvena Rowe's distinctive cuisine at Quìnce restaurant.*

Price Guide: (excluding VAT and breakfast)
king superior from £195
king deluxe from £225
studio suite from £325

Awards/Recognition: Condé Nast Johansens Most Excellent Bedroom 2012

Location: Green Park Underground, 1-min walk; St Pancras - Eurostar, 5 miles; Heathrow, 16 miles; Gatwick, 28 miles

Attractions: Green Park; Bond Street; Royal Academy; Buckingham Palace

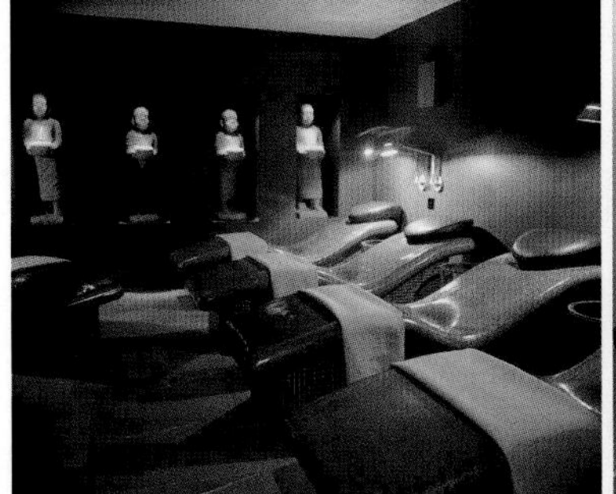

Stylish, contemporary and quirky, The May Fair takes 5-star luxury to another level. A legendary hotel with a glamorous past, it was first opened by King George V in 1927 and has played host to some of London's most extravagant society events. Bringing together smart and expressive modern design, outstanding service and exceptional attention to detail, the hotel fully deserves the CoolBrands award for the third year running, in recognition of its style and personality. A menu of over 40 expertly crafted signature drinks awaits in the renowned May Fair Bar, whilst Quìnce restaurant presents an innovative Eastern Mediterranean menu. The day spa, with its vast array of treatments, is the perfect antidote to a busy day of meetings or sightseeing, and where better to round off an eventful day than in the hotel's Palm Beach Casino, located in the former Grand Art Deco Ballroom, which offers entertainment until 6am.

Westbury Hotel

BOND STREET, MAYFAIR, LONDON W1S 2YF
Tel: 020 7629 7755 **International:** +44 (0)20 7629 7755
Web: www.condenastjohansens.com/westburymayfair **E-mail:** enquiries@westburymayfair.com

The 5-star luxury Westbury sits proudly in an enviable location just off Bond Street in the heart of London's fashionable Mayfair. The excellent personal service reflects the staff's passion to ensure every guest has a memorable stay. Complete with expert concierge and extremely adept and multi-lingual staff, this is the ideal choice for discerning guests from around the world. Bedrooms are luxuriously designed in warm tones and offer the utmost in comfort and style. As your day begins, there is no better way to start than with a Westbury breakfast and enjoy the splendour of calm and elegance in the luxurious Gallery Restaurant. A great way to start the evening is in the sophisticated Polo Bar with its impressive cocktail list and bar menu. You can see why this is popular with guests and Londoners alike.

Our inspector loved: *The location, service and cuisine overseen by Head Chef Alyn Williams, former Head Chef of 2 Michelin-Starred restaurants.*

Price Guide: (room only)
single £399
double £439
suite from £1099

Location: Bond Street Underground, 5-min walk; St Pancras - Eurostar, 4 miles; Heathrow Airport, 18 miles; Gatwick Airport, 30 miles

Attractions: Perfect shopping in the heart of Mayfair; West End Theatre's; National Gallery; London Eye

The New Linden Hotel

58 - 60 LEINSTER SQUARE, NOTTING HILL, LONDON W2 4PS
Tel: 020 7221 4321 **International:** +44 (0)20 7221 4321
Web: www.condenastjohansens.com/newlindenhotel **E-mail:** newlindenhotel@mayflower-group.co.uk

Our inspector loved: *The location, right in the heart of London's fashionable Notting Hill.*

Price Guide:
double £120-£155
suite £130-£195

 49    

Location: Notting Hill / Bayswater Tube, 5-min walk; Paddington Station, 1 mile; London Heathrow, 15 miles

Attractions: Madame Tussauds; Whiteleys of Bayswater; Hyde Park; Kensington Palace Gardens

The New Linden Hotel is a little gem with instant appeal. This pretty, white town house hotel is discovered in a peaceful residential street, in the heart of London's cosmopolitan Notting Hill, just a short walk from Portobello Road Market and within easy reach of tourist hot spots. The hotel's owners have transformed the building to suit the times without losing any of its Victorian charm. Once past the ornate entrance pillars you will find stylish bedrooms in colours of cream, brown, red and black, trendy minimal furnishings, high-tech entertainment units and stunning marble bathrooms. Not large, but with everything you could wish for. The lower ground floor breakfast room with its trendy wallpaper and freshly-prepared breakfast is a great place to start your day.

Sofitel London St James

6 WATERLOO PLACE, LONDON SW1Y 4AN

Tel: 020 7747 2200 **International:** +44 (0)20 7747 2200

Web: www.condenastjohansens.com/stjames **E-mail:** H3144@sofitel.com

Stylish, contemporary and very imposing, Sofitel London St James in central London is a Grade II listed building on the corner of Waterloo Place and Pall Mall. This 5-star hotel is the former home of the Cox's & King's bank, whose original artwork is still prominently displayed. The well-appointed bedrooms and suites have the smartest technology, including HD televisions. Black and white marble complements granite tops and chrome fittings in the bathrooms. French-British cuisine is trademark of the brasserie, The Balcon; while the renovated St James Bar offers a large selection of Champagnes and vintage cocktails. As for afternoon tea, you'll adore the eclectic Rose Lounge. You can also choose to relax in the stunningly designed Sofitel So SPA or perform a full work out in the So FIT gym.

Our inspector loved: *The fact that there is always something new to indulge in, whether it's the stunning spa, stylish bedrooms, buzzing bar or a new dining experience!*

Price Guide: (room only, excluding VAT)
single from £375
double from £425
suite £664-£1,800

Awards/Recognition: Condé Nast Traveller Readers' Spa Awards 2011, Best UK Hotel Spa and Top 25; Condé Nast Johansens Most Excellent Spa 2010

Location: Piccadilly Underground, 3-min walk; St Pancras - Eurostar, 3 miles; Heathrow, 16 miles; Gatwick, 28 miles

Attractions: Trafalgar Square; Buckingham Palace; London Eye; National Gallery; Burlington Arcade; Bond Street Shopping

London Syon Park, A Waldorf Astoria Hotel

SYON PARK, MIDDLESEX TW8 8JF
Tel: 020 7870 7777 **International:** +44 (0)20 7870 7777
Web: www.condenastjohansens.com/londonsyonpark **E-mail:** syonpark.info@waldorfastoria.com

Our inspector loved: *The chic modern décor, fabulous rooms and unique green London location.*

Price Guide:
single £209-£399
double £249-£439
presidential suite £2,999-£3,169

 137 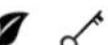   30   SPA

Location: A4, ½ mile; Richmond, 3 miles; Central London, 7 miles; London Heathrow, 8 miles

Attractions: Syon House and Park; Kew Gardens; Richmond; Twickenham Stadium

Luxurious contemporary design meets English charm at this fabulously sophisticated new London hotel. Part of the legendary Waldorf Astoria dynasty, the exceptional estate offers unsurpassed service and access to Syon Park, which sits at the edge of the magnificent 200-acre Syon House Estate and has been the playground for English aristocracy for over 400 years. The rooms and suites are inviting and graceful with views over the hotel's pools and gardens. Don't miss the fabulous cocktails at Peacock Alley before dining at The Capability restaurant or enjoying tapas at the more private Clubhouse. Young and old alike will love Brownies where fabulous pastry and ice cream creations are served, and a visit to the edible garden is a must! Those wishing to completely unwind can do so at Kallima Spa, whilst active guests can try their hand at archery, yoga, laser clay pigeon shooting, golf, fishing on the lake and more.

51 Buckingham Gate, Taj Suites and Residences

51 BUCKINGHAM GATE, WESTMINSTER, LONDON SW1E 6AF
Tel: 020 7769 7766 **International:** +44 (0)20 7769 7766
Web: www.condenastjohansens.com/buckinghamgate **E-mail:** reservations@51-buckinghamgate.co.uk

This exceptional Victorian period town house is a 5 AA Red Star - Inspectors Choice hotel. In the heart of Westminster, just minutes from Buckingham Palace, it is complete with an award-winning, magical courtyard garden. The contemporary design combines subtle, state-of-the-art technology with impeccable service. The rooms are equally impressive and range from junior suites to the impressive Prime Minister's Residence and Presidential Residence. You can indulge in the Spa at 51 exclusively, which offers Anne Sémonin treatments or use the many other wonderful amenities including the gymnasium, saunas and steam rooms. The room service is 24 hours and nothing is too much trouble for the highly trained staff. Try the mouth watering Michelin-Starred Quilon for a unique and delicious dining experience. Be brave and let the chef choose for you.

Our inspector loved: *The strikingly decorated suites.*

Price Guide: (excluding breakfast and VAT)
suites £255–£7,250
prime minister's residence upon request
presidential residence upon request

Awards/Recognition: 1 Star Michelin 2012 (Quilon Restaurant)

Location: St James's Park Underground Station, 5-min walk; Victoria Station, 10-min walk; St Pancras, Eurostar, 5 miles; Heathrow Airport, 16 miles; Gatwick Airport, 28 miles

Attractions: Buckingham Palace; St James's Park; Houses of Parliament; London Eye

THE TALBOT HOTEL

NEW STREET, OUNDLE, NORTHAMPTONSHIRE PE8 4EA
Tel: 01832 273621 **International:** +44 (0)1832 273621
Web: www.condenastjohansens.com/talbotoudle **E-mail:** talbot@bpcmail.co.uk

Our inspector loved: *The central location of this recently re-opened hotel.*

Price Guide:
single £95
double £125-£165
suite £195

Location: A605, ½ mile; A14, 7 miles; A1, 8 miles

Attractions: Belvoir Castle; Nene Valley; Rutland Water; Lyveden New Bield (National Trust); Elton Hall and Gardens

A warm, friendly and professionally run historic hotel, The Talbot Hotel, Eatery & Coffee House is situated in the heart of the beautiful market town of Oundle, within the picturesque, unspoilt Nene Valley. The site's history dates back to 638AD when it was a hostelry run by monks offering food, drink and shelter to those visiting the monastery. The present 17th-century building was rebuilt in stone and transferred from Fotheringhay and has recently undergone a major refurbishment. Offering an exceedingly high standard, plenty of history remains including the staircase from Fotheringhay Castle; allegedly that which Mary Queen of Scots was led down to her execution. Each comfortable guest room and suite is individually styled and 3 meeting rooms are available. On the ground floor is the conservatory with roaring open fires and views of the courtyard and Tudor entrance, and the restaurant serving afternoon tea, lunches and dinners prepared from the finest local produce.

Hambleton Hall

HAMBLETON, OAKHAM, RUTLAND LE15 8TH
Tel: 01572 756991 **International:** +44 (0)1572 756991
Web: www.condenastjohansens.com/hambletonhall **E-mail:** hotel@hambletonhall.com

Originally a Victorian mansion, Hambleton Hall celebrated its 30th year as an exceptional lakeside hotel in 2010, and continues to attract acclaim for achieving near perfection. Artful blends of flowers from local hedgerows and London flower markets add splashes of colour to the bedrooms. The Croquet Pavilion a 2-bedroom suite with living and breakfast rooms is a luxurious additional option. In the Michelin-Starred restaurant, Chef Aaron Patterson and his brigade offer strongly seasonal menus - grouse, Scottish ceps, chanterelles, partridge and woodcock all appear when they're supposed to, accompanied by vegetables, herbs and salads from the Hall's garden. If you're feeling energetic you can embark on walks around the lake and there are opportunities for tennis, swimming, golf, cycling and sailing, otherwise you can browse for hidden treasures in Oakham's antique shops.

***Our inspector loved:** Experiencing perfection - the welcome, the service, the accommodation, the food, the location!*

Price Guide: single from £195
double/twin £255–£425
suite £530–£635

Awards/Recognition: Condé Nast Johansens Most Excellent Hotel 2011; 1 Star Michelin 2012; AA Wine Award & Overall 2010-2011; 4 AA Rosettes 2012-2013; Harden's Top 10 Restaurants 2012

Location: A606, 2 miles; Oakham, 2 miles; A1(M), 10 miles; East Midlands International Airport, 40 miles

Attractions: Hambleton Bakery; Rutland Water; Burghley House; Rockingham Castle

Hoar Cross Hall Spa Resort

HOAR CROSS, NEAR YOXALL, STAFFORDSHIRE DE13 8QS
Tel: 01283 575671 **International:** +44 (0)1283 575671
Web: www.condenastjohansens.com/hoarcrosshall **E-mail:** info@hoarcross.co.uk

Our inspector loved: *This excellent fully-inclusive spa resort with extensive facilities and spa treatments.*

Price Guide: (Including 2 lunches, à la carte dinner and breakfast, based on 2 people sharing)
from £130 per person

Location: A515, 2 miles; A50, 8 miles; Lichfield, 8 miles; M6 jct 12 or 15, 22 miles

Attractions: In the heart of The National Forest; Historic Lichfield

Welcome to the only stately home spa resort hotel in England and winner of England's Leading Resort, World Travel Awards 2005-2011. Surrounded by 100 acres of pretty landscaped gardens, the interior is equally beautiful with a traditional yet refreshing décor of oak panelling, tapestries, rich furnishings and paintings. The Jacobean staircase leads to the bedrooms, which all contain crown tester beds, and penthouses with private saunas and balconies; many have hot tubs overlooking the treetops. A superb à la carte menu is served in the ballroom where gilded ceilings and William Morris wallpaper set the scene. Trained experts are ready to assist with yoga, meditation, t'ai chi, Pilates, dance classes and aqua-aerobics. The spa has sea water and hydrotherapy pools, flotation therapy baths, saunas, steam rooms, water grottos, saunariums, an aromatherapy room, 4000 sq ft gym, aerobics, yoga suites and over 100 treatment choices. A PGA golf academy is also available.

THE GRAND HOTEL

KING EDWARD'S PARADE, EASTBOURNE, EAST SUSSEX BN21 4EQ
Tel: 01323 412345 **International:** +44 (0)1323 412345
Web: www.condenastjohansens.com/grandeastbourne **E-mail:** reservations@grandeastbourne.com

A lasting reminder of the Victorian period, the delightful façade of The Grand Hotel conceals reception rooms adorned with rich fabrics. Many of the 152 bedrooms have vast proportions, and each has been refurbished to include every comfort. There are numerous places in which to relax, and a good choice of restaurants and bars - the Mirabelle in particular achieves exceptional standards of fine dining. Health Club and Spa facilities include indoor and outdoor pools, a gym, sauna, spa bath, steam room, snooker tables, hair salon and 8 treatment rooms featuring the Kerstin Florian skin care range and Vitaman, a specially created male grooming product. If you are seeking a peaceful retreat you'll be more than happy with the tranquil atmosphere at The Grand Hotel with its impeccably delivered standards of traditional service. Pastimes include golf at a nearby club, walks along the downs, sea fishing and visits to nearby theatres.

Our inspector loved: *The luxury and excellent service of this still very grand hotel that offers every modern convenience. This is a wonderful place to stay.*

Price Guide:
double/twin £199–£350
suite £400–£555

Awards/Recognition: Condé Nast Johansens Most Excellent Waterside Hotel 2012; 2 AA Rosettes 2012-2013

Location: On the Seafront; A22, 7.5 miles; M23 jct 11, 40 miles; Gatwick Airport, 48 miles

Attractions: South Downs Way National Park; The English Wine Centre; Three Theatres; Glyndebourne Opera

Ashdown Park Hotel and Country Club

WYCH CROSS, FOREST ROW, EAST SUSSEX RH18 5JR
Tel: 01342 824988 **International:** +44 (0)1342 824988
Web: www.condenastjohansens.com/ashdownpark **E-mail:** reservations@ashdownpark.com

Our inspector loved: *The fascinating history and grandeur of this beautiful county house hotel.*

Price Guide:
double/twin £199-£380
suite £420–£465

Awards/Recognition: 2 AA Rosettes 2012-2013

Location: A22, 0.5 miles; M25 jct 6, 15 miles; East Grinstead, 5 miles; Gatwick Airport, 16 miles

Attractions: Ashdown Forest; Bluebell Railway; Wakehurst Place Gardens; Lingfield Park Racecourse

Set in 186 acres of East Sussex countryside, surrounded by woodland walks, free roaming deer and utter tranquillity, Ashdown Park Hotel and Country Club is ideal for those wishing to de-stress from everyday life. Whether visiting with the family or getting away with a loved one, there are 8 guest room categories to choose from; each luxuriously appointed. Relax at The Revitalise Spa and enjoy its range of pampering and relaxing treatments from the Kerstin Florian skin care range and Vitaman, a specifically created male grooming product. And enjoy the complimentary amenities of The Country Club with indoor swimming pool, steam room, sauna and 18 hole, par 3 golf course. Guests feeling particularly energetic can make use of the gym, play a game of tennis or take a jog along one of the many running trails. Complete the perfect day by dining at the 2 AA Rosette-awarded Anderida Restaurant where a resident pianist and wonderful views set the scene.

Horsted Place Country House Hotel

LITTLE HORSTED, EAST SUSSEX TN22 5TS
Tel: 01825 750581 **International:** +44 (0)1825 750581
Web: www.condenastjohansens.com/horstedplace **E-mail:** hotel@horstedplace.co.uk

The country estate of Horsted Place sits amidst the serene Sussex Downs in the south of England. Beyond the splendid Victorian gothic architecture, built in 1851, is an interior predominantly styled by the celebrated Victorian architect, Augustus Pugin. In former years the Queen and Prince Philip were frequent visitors. Guests today are invited to enjoy the excellent service offered by a committed staff. Chef Allan Garth offers a daily fixed price menu as well as a seasonal à la carte menu. The Terrace Room is an elegant and airy private function room, licensed for weddings for up to 100 guests. The smaller Morning Room and Library are ideal for boardroom-style meetings and intimate dinner parties, and the self-contained management centre offers privacy and exclusivity for business meetings in a contemporary setting.

Our inspector loved: *The fine gothic architecture, beautiful grounds and friendly service - a perfect combination.*

Price Guide:
double from £145
suite from £225

Awards/Recognition: 2 AA Rosette 2012-2013

Location: On the A26; M23 jct 10, 20 miles; Lewes, 6 miles; Gatwick, 25 miles

Attractions: Glyndebourne Opera; Sheffield Park Gardens; Bluebell Railway; East Sussex National Golf Course

Newick Park Hotel & Country Estate

NEWICK, NEAR LEWES, EAST SUSSEX BN8 4SB
Tel: 01825 723633 **International:** +44 (0)1825 723633
Web: www.condenastjohansens.com/newickpark **E-mail:** bookings@newickpark.co.uk

Our inspector loved: *The rural location and welcoming atmosphere.*

Price Guide:
single from £125
double/twin from £165

Awards/Recognition: Condé Nast Johansens Taittinger Wine List Award, Best Value for Money 2012; Condé Nast Johansens Readers' Award 2011; 2 AA Rosettes 2012-2013

Location: A272, 1 mile; M23 jct 11, 18 miles; Lewes, 8 miles; Gatwick Airport, 28 miles

Attractions: Sheffield Park Garden and Wakehurst Place; Opera at Glyndebourne; Regency Brighton; Bluebell Railway

This magnificent Grade II* listed Georgian house is set in over 200 acres of beautiful parkland and landscaped gardens overlooking the Longford River and South Downs. Whilst Newick Park is situated in a convenient location near to the main road and rail routes and only 30 minutes from Gatwick Airport, the hotel maintains an atmosphere of complete tranquillity and privacy. Bedrooms are decorated in a classic style featuring elegant antiques and friendly staff ensure that you receive a warm welcome. The exquisite dining room offers culinary delights carefully prepared by Head Chef Chris Moore. The house and grounds are ideal for weddings, conferences and private parties and The Dell gardens primarily planted in Victorian times include a rare collection of Royal Ferns. Exclusive use can be arranged by appointment.

BAILIFFSCOURT HOTEL & SPA

CLIMPING, ARUNDEL, WEST SUSSEX BN17 5RW
Tel: 01903 723511 **International:** +44 (0)1903 723511
Web: www.condenastjohansens.com/bailiffscourt **E-mail:** bailiffscourt@hshotels.co.uk

Step back in time at Bailiffscourt, a perfectly preserved "medieval" manor with outbuildings. Built in the 1930s using authentic material salvaged from historic old buildings, this luxurious hotel features narled 15th-century beams and gothic mullioned windows that recreate the Middle Ages. Many luxurious rooms offer four-poster beds, open log fires and beautiful views across the surrounding countryside. Menus are varied, and in summer you can eat out in the rose-clad courtyard or walled garden. The award-winning health spa features an outdoor Californian hot tub, indoor spa pool, sauna, gym, hammocks and 6 beauty rooms. 2 tennis courts and a croquet lawn complete the on-site leisure facilities, while a private pathway leads 100 yards down to Climping Beach, ideal for your morning walk.

Our inspector loved: *The sumptuous Baylies room, which is a must for a romantic break by the Sussex Coast.*

Price Guide: (including dinner)
single from £180
double from £240
feature from £410

Awards/Recognition: 2 AA Rosettes 2012-2013

Location: A259, 1 mile; M27 jct 1, 30 miles; Arundel, 6 miles; Gatwick Airport, 44 miles

Attractions: Arundel Castle; Goodwood Estate; Chichester Festival Theatre; Clymping Beach

Ockenden Manor Hotel & Spa

OCKENDEN LANE, CUCKFIELD, WEST SUSSEX RH17 5LD
Tel: 01444 416111 **International:** +44 (0)1444 416111
Web: www.condenastjohansens.com/ockendenmanor **E-mail:** ockenden@hshotels.co.uk

Our inspector loved: *The beautiful and newly opened spa and adjoining rooms that has just made Ockenden Manor even better!*

Price Guide:
single from £121
double £190–£350
suite £330–£395

Awards/Recognition: 1 Star Michelin 2012; 3 AA Rosettes 2012-2013

Location: A272, 0.5 mile; M23 jct 10, 4 miles; Haywards Heath, 2 miles; Gatwick Airport, 18 miles

Attractions: Wakehurst and Nymans Gardens; Glyndebourne Opera; Regency Brighton; Bluebell Railway

History and character abound in this enchanting Elizabethan manor house hotel, which was first recorded in 1520. Tucked away in one of the prettiest Tudor villages in the country, it is ideal for exploring Sussex and Kent. From the minute you step through its doors, you're swept away by warm hospitality and culinary delights. 28 distinctive bedrooms and suites offer an array of fascinating features: climb the private staircase to Elizabeth, indulge in a Victorian-style bath in Hugh, or enjoy the huge four-poster bed in Charles. The romantic restaurant, with its sweeping vistas across the garden and beyond, is the perfect setting to enjoy innovative, Michelin-Starred cuisine and an inspired wine list. Guests in need of pampering will adore the new spa set within the walled gardens with stunning views across a wooded valley. Its facilities include an indoor-outdoor swimming pool, rainforest walk through shower, sauna, steam room, hot tub, relaxation room, gym and treatment rooms.

PARK HOUSE HOTEL & PH_2O SPA

BEPTON, MIDHURST, WEST SUSSEX GU29 0JB
Tel: 01730 819 000 **International:** +44 (0)1730 819 000
Web: www.condenastjohansens.com/parkhousehotel **E-mail:** reservations@parkhousehotel.com

Park House Hotel is a quintessential English country house hotel located in 10 acres of South Downs National Park, an area of outstanding natural beauty, close to the historic market town of Midhurst. Family run and family friendly, this home-from-home hotel is warm and welcoming with a designer touch. Most guest rooms look out to stunning views of the surrounding rose garden, ponds, croquet and bowls lawns, golf course and swimming pool. And within these pretty grounds are 3 private cottages that can be reserved for exclusive use. 2 have a kitchen, however, the seasonal, locally sourced dishes at the hotel's restaurant are irresistible and its menu always features English favourites. A restored Sussex barn, located next to the main house, is a superb venue for a party, business meeting or wedding reception, and let's not forget the PH_2O spa, a state-of-the-art therapeutic, fitness and luxury facility offering a variety of packages and services.

Our inspector loved: *The fantastic spa and luxurious bedrooms of this intimate country house.*

Price Guide:
single £135
double £135-£224
suite £240-£360

Location: Gatwick Airport, 37 miles; Heathrow Airport, 45 miles; A3, 12 miles; A27, 13 miles

Attractions: Weald and Downland Open Air Museum; Petworth House; Goodwood Racecourse and Estate; Cowdray Ruins

THE SPREAD EAGLE HOTEL & SPA

SOUTH STREET, MIDHURST, WEST SUSSEX GU29 9NH
Tel: 01730 816911 **International:** +44 (0)1730 816911
Web: www.condenastjohansens.com/spreadeaglemidhurst **E-mail:** spreadeagle@hshotels.co.uk

Our inspector loved: *The fine food, incredible history and great location for exploring the Sussex countryside.*

Price Guide: (including dinner)
single from £125-£390
double from £190-£390
suite from £290

Awards/Recognition: Condé Nast Johansens Most Excellent Value for Money 2012; 2 AA Rosettes 2012-2013

Location: Town Centre; Just off A272/286, 0.2 miles; M25 jct 9, 31 miles; Gatwick Airport, 38 miles

Attractions: Petworth House; Cowdray Park; Goodwood House and Estate; Chichester Cathedral; West Dean Gardens

The historic Spread Eagle Hotel is one of England's oldest hotels, dating from 1430 and rich in charm and period features cleverly mixed with modern luxuries. This West Sussex hotel is perfect for a luxury spa break: it boasts an outstanding modern spa with an impressive vaulted glass ceiling and plenty of wet areas. In the restaurant Nathan Marshall creates a modern classic menu using seasonal flavours and plenty of local produce. The bedrooms are delightful, many with antiques and some with four-poster beds. The White Room contains a "secret passage" and is said to have been used by smugglers in their attempt to evade the King's men. With easy access to Sussex and the South Downs, this is a great area to explore whether walking, shopping or enjoying any number of outdoor activities, after which a cream tea at the Spread Eagle will be well deserved. Childrens' high-teas can be arranged and well-behaved dogs are allowed in some bedrooms.

Gravetye Manor

VOWELS LANE, NEAR WEST HOATHLY, WEST SUSSEX RH19 4LJ
Tel: 01342 810567 **International:** +44 (0)1342 810567
Web: www.condenastjohansens.com/gravetyemanor **E-mail:** info@gravetyemanor.co.uk

Drive a mile through private Sussex woods to find this enchanting Elizabethan manor house hotel steeped in history. Friendly and unstuffy, with a welcoming atmosphere, Gravetye is surrounded by 35 acres of renowned gardens with fine stone walls. This was the former home of gardener and pioneer William Robinson until 1935, and it was here that he realised many of his ideals for the creation of The English Natural Garden. The house and its interiors more than live up to this standard with 17 beautifully appointed rooms ranging from standard to de luxe. In the intimate, oak-panelled restaurant enjoy the "modern British" cuisine of highly-acclaimed Chef Rupert Gleadow. Rupert prides himself on the use of locally sourced organic produce where possible, with much grown on Gravetye's own garden and local farms. Run by a young team of dedicated professionals, the hotel's service is impeccable, and it can host meetings, special events and civil wedding ceremonies.

Our inspector loved: *The wonderful food and beautiful gardens that make this classic country house a perfect retreat.*

Price Guide:
standard £240-£290
superior £280-£315
de luxe £355-£430

Awards/Recognition: 3 AA Rosettes 2012-2013

Location: East Grinstead Station, 4 miles; Gatwick Airport, 13 miles; M25 jct 6, 14 miles

Attractions: Royal Ashdown Golf Course; Wakehurst Place; Hever Castle; Standen (National Trust)

Nailcote Hall

NAILCOTE LANE, BERKSWELL, NEAR SOLIHULL, WARWICKSHIRE CV7 7DE
Tel: 02476 466174 **International:** +44 (0)2476 466174
Web: www.condenastjohansens.com/nailcotehall **E-mail:** info@nailcotehall.co.uk

Our inspector loved: *The picturesque and challenging par 3 golf course matched by comfortable hospitality in the hotel.*

Price Guide:
single £185
double/twin £200
suite £200–£305

Location: A452, 2 miles; M42 jct 5, 7 miles; Balsall Common, 3 miles; Birmingham International Airport, 9 miles

Attractions: Warwick Castle; Kenilworth Castle; Coventry Cathedral; Royal Leamington Spa; Stratford-Upon-Avon

Located in the heart of England, Nailcote Hall is a charming hotel that dates back to Elizabethan times. Built in 1640, Oliver Cromwell and his troops used this now fully restored country house hotel during the Civil War. The intimate Tudor surrounds of the Oak Room restaurant, the luxury accommodation and impressive leisure facilities are all enticing features.These include a Roman-style swimming pool, gym, solarium and steam room, outside all-weather tennis courts, pétanque, croquet, a challenging 9-hole par 3 golf course and putting green - host to the "British Par 3 Championship". Nailcote Hall is within 15 minutes' drive of the castle towns of Kenilworth and Warwick, Coventry Cathedral, Birmingham International Airport/Station and the NEC.

Lucknam Park Hotel & Spa

COLERNE, CHIPPENHAM, WILTSHIRE SN14 8AZ
Tel: 01225 742777 **International:** +44 (0)1225 742777
Web: www.condenastjohansens.com/lucknampark **E-mail:** reservations@lucknampark.co.uk

Lucknam Park country house hotel in Bath is a spectacular Palladian mansion set within a 500-acre private estate 6 miles from the historic city of Bath. A majestic 5-star luxury hotel, boasting the award-winning restaurant The Park (it is recommended that you book in advance) that delivers both elegant sophistication and the warm comfort of an English country house. The acclaimed spa is exceptional, with its clean lines of natural materials fused with floor-to-ceiling windows lends itself to total relaxation. Features include a 20-metre heated pool, indoor-outdoor hydrotherapy pool, thermal cabins and 9 state-of-the-art treatment rooms using products from Anne Sémonin and Carita, Paris. Here, there is also a stylish and contemporary Brasserie featuring an open kitchen. For the more energetic there is an Equestrian Centre, 2 floodlit tennis courts, a five-a-side football pitch, croquet lawn and mountain bikes.

Our inspector loved: *The "wow" factor at every turn, the excellent service, contemporary spa and luxurious accommodation.*

Price Guide: (room only)
single/double/twin from £345
suite from £760

Awards/Recognition: Condé Nast Johansens Most Excellent Spa 2011; 1 Star Michelin 2012; Relais & Châteaux; 3 AA Rosettes 2012-2013

Location: A420, 1.5 miles; M4 jct 18, 9 miles; Bristol, 20 miles

Attractions: Bath; Lacock; Castle Combe; Westonbirt Arboretum; Longleat

WHATLEY MANOR

EASTON GREY, MALMESBURY, WILTSHIRE SN16 0RB
Tel: 01666 822888 **International:** +44 (0)1666 822888
Web: www.condenastjohansens.com/whatley **E-mail:** reservations@whatleymanor.com

Our inspector loved: *The excellent service, warm welcome and private luxury.*

Price Guide: (including full English breakfast, daily newspaper, use of spa facilities and 10% discretionary service charge)
standard from £305
superior/deluxe £375-£515
suite £665-£865

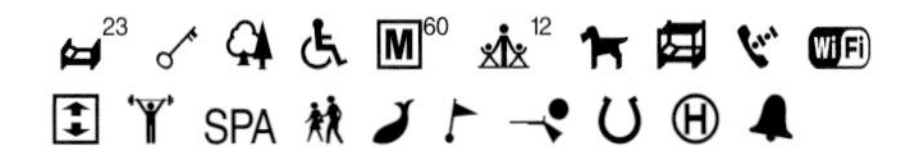

Awards/Recognition: 2 Star Michelin 2012; Condé Nast Johansens Most Excellent Restaurant for "The Dining Room" 2012; Relais & Châteaux Grand Chef; 4 AA Rosettes 2012-2013

Location: Off the B4040; A429, 3 miles; M4 jct 17, 8 miles; London, 75-min train

Attractions: The Cotswolds; Bath; Malmesbury Abbey and Gardens; Tetbury; Westonbirt Arboretum

Looking to book a spa break, enjoy an award-winning gastronomic experience or simply relax in luxurious surroundings? Then this beautifully designed, stylish and sophisticated retreat nestling in 12 acres of Wiltshire countryside on the doorstep to the Cotswolds is for you. Very careful attention to detail is evident throughout the 15 bedrooms and 8 suites furnished with Italian furniture and handmade French wallpaper, each entirely individual. The atmosphere is welcoming and feels more like a family-owned country home. There are 2 gastronomic experiences on offer: the 2 Michelin-Starred restaurant, The Dining Room; and the more informal brasserie, "Le Mazot" with its refreshingly alternative Swiss interior. The highly-acclaimed spa, Aquarias, includes one of the largest hydrotherapy pools in the UK and a La Prairie "Art of Beauty" Centre. A private cinema accommodates up to 40 people and the 12 acres of gardens have 26 distinct areas for you to explore.

THE DORMY

WILLERSEY HILL, BROADWAY, WORCESTERSHIRE WR12 7LF
Tel: 01386 852711 **International:** +44 (0)1386 852711
Web: www.condenastjohansens.com/dormyhouse **E-mail:** reservations@dormyhouse.co.uk

A charming home-from-home with more than a dash of panache,The Dormy is a tastefully converted farmhouse that dates back to the 17th century in the heart of the fairy tale Cotswolds. It's a haven of luxury for anyone who loves to relax, indulge and enjoy life. Behind its mellow stone walls is a welcoming intimate warmth. Think roaring log fires, deep comfy sofas and cosy leather armchairs: The Dormy is a graceful and established country house hotel. Laid-back elegance is the premise of the individually-designed bedrooms and suites. Their comfort is typified by crisp bed linen and plump pillows, and unique character is created by a harmonious mix of traditional English furniture and rich fabrics. Nothing is too much trouble at The Dormy, where a long-serving team of staff delivers impeccable but unstuffy service. Whatever you do, make sure you dine in the delightful 2 Rosette-awarded Dining Room, or the equally fine Bar/Brasserie.

Our inspector loved: *The picturesque location of this charming Cotswold hotel, sitting on the top of Fish Hill with views over the Vale of Evesham.*

Price Guide:
single from £230
double/twin from £250
suite from £295

Awards/Recognition: 2 AA Rosettes 2012-2013

Location: A44, ¼ mile; Broadway, 3 miles; M40 jct 8 or 15, 25 miles; Birmingham International Airport, 41 miles

Attractions: The Cotswolds; Cheltenham; Stratford-upon-Avon; Hidcote Manor; Kiftsgate Gardens

Simonstone Hall

HAWES, NORTH YORKSHIRE DL8 3LY
Tel: 01969 667255 **International:** +44 (0)1969 667255
Web: www.condenastjohansens.com/simonstonehall **E-mail:** enquiries@simonstonehall.com

Our inspector loved: *The wonderful setting with stunning views across Upper Wensleydale.*

Price Guide:
single £75–£175
double/twin £100–£195

Location: A684, 1.5 miles; Hawes, 1.5 miles; M6 jct 37, 30-min drive; A1M, 40-min drive

Attractions: Hardraw Force; Wensleydale Creamery Cheese Factory; Yorkshire Dales; Bolton Castle

Simonstone Hall is one of the finest Yorkshire Dales hotels with wonderful views of Wensleydale. A former 18th-century hunting lodge, the Hall has been lovingly restored and furnished with antiques to create a romantic hotel perfect for wedding receptions and is an idyllic, memorable retreat. Standing in a beautiful setting adjacent to 4,000 acres of grouse moors and upland grazing, many of the building's period features have been retained such as the panelled dining room, mahogany staircase with ancestral stained-glass windows and a lounge with ornamental ceilings. The bedrooms are of a high standard, 4 offer four-poster comfort and 2 have sleigh beds. The formal dining room, with its stunning views across Upper Wensleydale, serves an à la carte menu composed of the freshest local produce along with an excellent wine list to complement any dish. Warm, informal dining and traditional cuisine can be enjoyed in The Pub and The Brasserie.

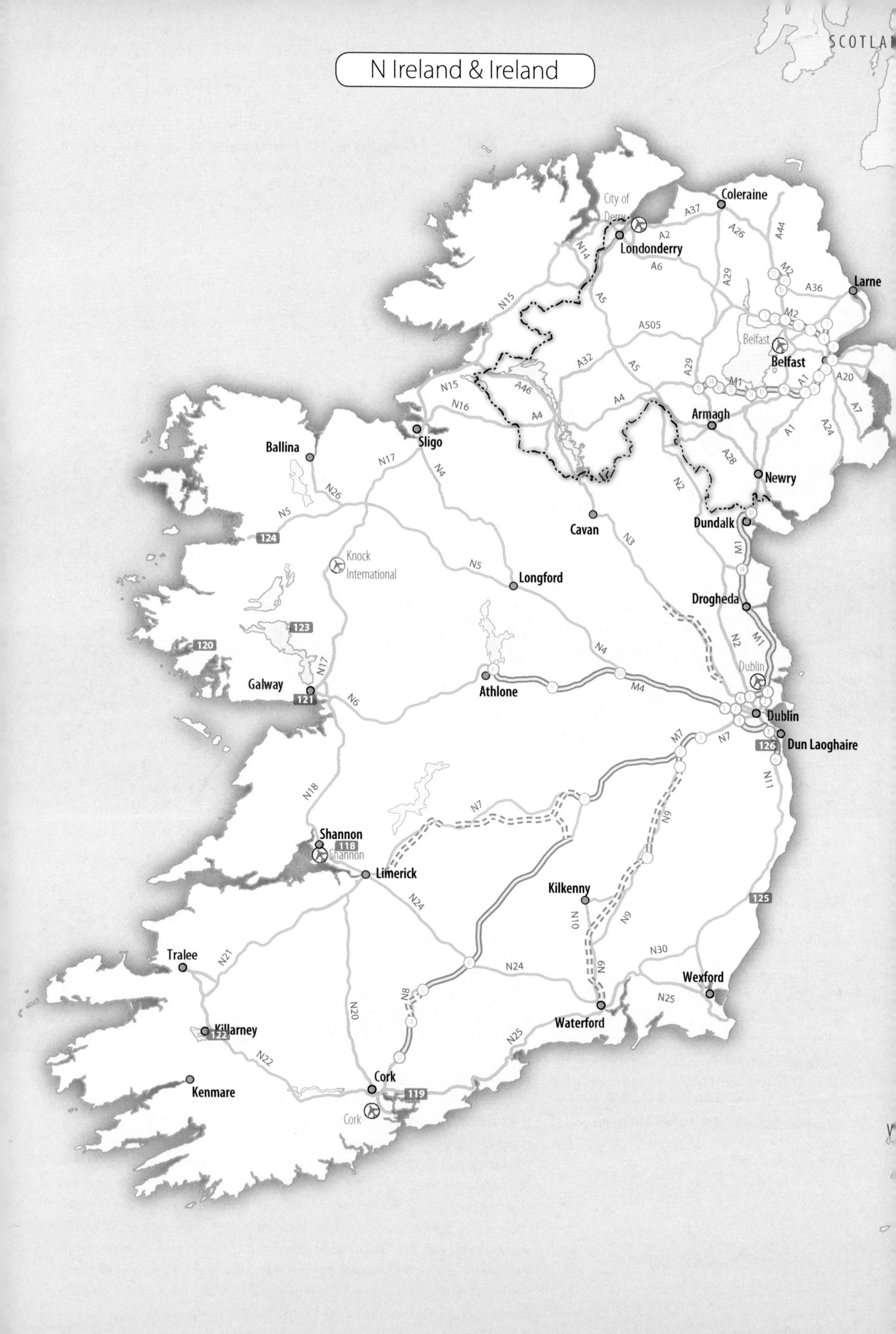
N Ireland & Ireland
SCOTLA
City of Derry
Coleraine
Londonderry
Larne
Belfast
Belfast
Armagh
Newry
Dundalk
Cavan
Sligo
Ballina
Knock International
Longford
Drogheda
Dublin
Dublin
Dun Laoghaire
Galway
Athlone
Shannon
Shannon
Limerick
Kilkenny
Tralee
Killarney
Kenmare
Cork
Cork
Waterford
Wexford
A37
A2
A26
A44
A6
A29
M2
A36
A5
A505
A32
A46
A4
M1
A1
A20
A7
A24
A28
N2
N3
N4
N5
N6
N7
N8
N9
N10
N11
N14
N15
N16
N17
N18
N20
N21
N22
N24
N25
N26
N30
M4
M7
118
119
120
121
122
123
124
125
126

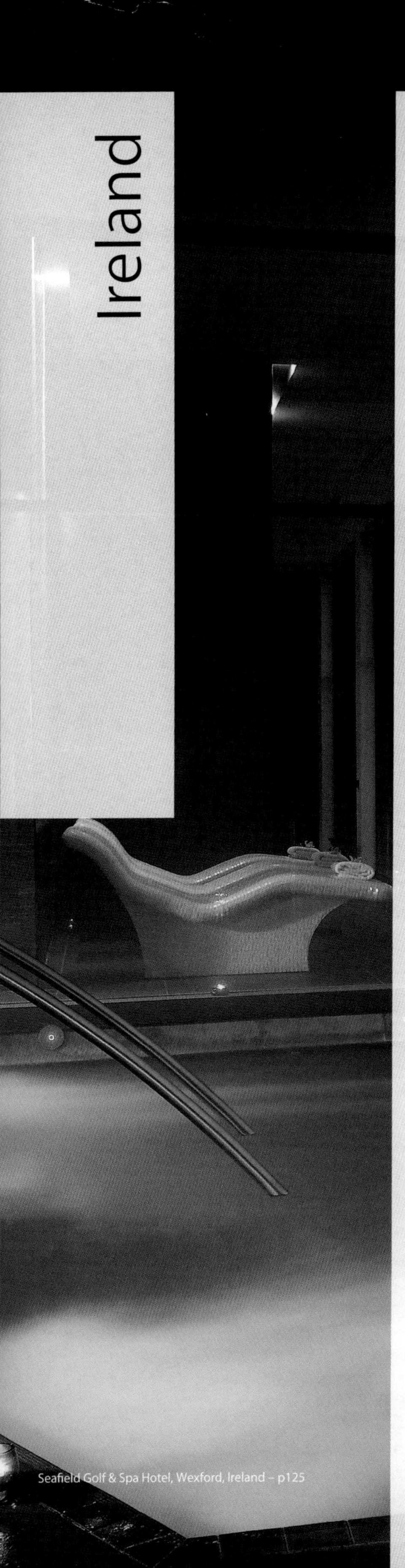

Seafield Golf & Spa Hotel, Wexford, Ireland – p125

For further information on Ireland, please contact:

The Irish Tourist Board
(Bord Fáilte Eíreann)
Tel: 0800 313 4000
www.discoverireland.com

Tourism Ireland
Tel: +353 (0)1476 3400
www.tourismireland.com

Irish Georgian Society
74 Merrion Square
Dublin 2
Tel: +353 (0)1676 7053
www.ige.ie

Irish Ferries
Tel: 0818 300400
www.irishferries.com

Aer Lingus
Ireland Tel: 0818 365044
GB and Northern Ireland Tel: 0871 718 2020
www.aerlingus.com

or see **pages 155-158** for details of local historic houses, castles and gardens to visit during your stay.

For additional places to stay in Ireland turn to **pages 149-153** where a listing of our Recommended Small Hotels, Inns & Restaurants Guide can be found.

UNIVERSITY COLLEGE BIRMINGHAM

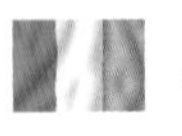

DROMOLAND CASTLE

NEWMARKET-ON-FERGUS, CO CLARE
Tel: 00 353 61368144
Web: www.condenastjohansens.com/dromolandcastle **E-mail:** sales@dromoland.ie

Arriving at this majestic hotel is like stepping into a fairy tale. Dromoland Castle is one of the most impressive and magical castle hotels in Ireland with a fascinating history dating back to the 16th century when it was the residence of the O'Brien clan. In their possession for 18 generations, the baronial sumptuousness of the interior design befits its history, and is wonderfully combined with contemporary conveniences. Attentive staff provide service fit for a king! There is no doubt that you will feel pampered and relaxed. Sink into a comfy chair and read a good book by the fireside before heading off to the spa, an intimate haven within the heart of the castle, complete with indoor pool and sauna. Delicious dishes inspired by seasonal produce and Irish tradition are served in restaurant; you can even have a luxury picnic basket prepared.

Our inspector loved: *The overwhelming sense of history, with style and exemplary service in abundance.*

Price Guide: (euro, room only)
single/double €225–€573
suite €471–€955

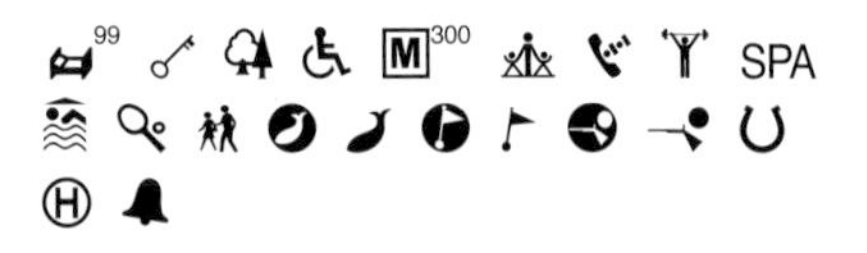

Location: Just off the N18; Limerick, 19 miles; Shannon Airport, 8 miles

Attractions: Dramatic West Coast; The Cliffs of Moher and The Buren Region; Galway City and The Aran Islands; Bunratty Castle and Folk Park; King John's Castle

Castlemartyr Resort

CASTLEMARTYR, CO CORK
Tel: 00 353 21 4219000
Web: www.condenastjohansens.com/castlemartyr **E-mail:** reservations@castlemartyrresort.ie

Our inspector loved: *The attention to detail, locally produced ingredients for great dishes and a relaxing spa.*

Price Guide: (euro)
single €140-€215
double €150-€225
suite €225-€1305

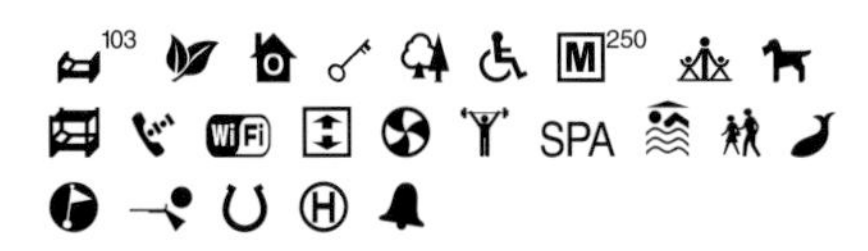

Location: Midleton, 6 miles; Cork City, 18 miles; Cork Airport, 22 miles; Dungarven, 27 miles

Attractions: Kinsale; Titanic Trail, Cobh; Old Jameson Distillery; Fota Wildlife Park; English Market

Past a gently meandering river, you will come upon the 5-star luxury Castlemartyr Resort, an exquisite hotel that dates back to the 17th century and today, exudes luxury and elegance complemented by a high standard of service. The opulent bedrooms are impeccably styled with a handsome combination of antiques, lavish fabrics and every modern amenity. The spa is unlike any other: a spacious and light idyll where you can leave your worries behind and indulge in a rejuvenating treatment. Do not miss the pleasure of the restaurant's innovative cuisine! The ingredients are fresh, locally produced and of exceptional quality. During the day, explore the countless delights of this large country estate, with its rolling hills, mature woodlands, tranquil lake teeming with wildlife and stunning golf course. Take a stroll, enjoy a game of croquet, or simply relax and admire your surroundings.

Cashel House

CASHEL, CONNEMARA, CO GALWAY
Tel: 00 353 95 31001
Web: www.condenastjohansens.com/cashelhouse **E-mail:** res@cashel-house-hotel.com

Surrounded by exotic flowering gardens and woodland walks at the head of Cashel Bay, this pretty hotel was built in 1840 for Captain Thomas Hazel, an English landowner, by the owners' great, great grandfather. Today, the McEvilly family welcome you to their tastefully furnished home where turf and log fires invite you to relax and comfortable bedrooms and suites offer hill or garden views. In the dining room the ever-changing menus of imaginative dishes feature local seafood, lamb, beef, game and home-grown vegetables alongside a carefully chosen wine list. Outside, the stunning surrounds offer a plethora of activities such as golf, fishing, bird watching, hill walking and mountain hiking. And furthermore, Cashel House has its very own beach, on-site stud farm and 50 acres of award-winning gardens where various 2 and 3-day gardening courses, including garden design, restoration, vegetable, herb and fruit growing take place.

Our inspector loved: *The beautiful surrounding gardens of this totally unspoilt oasis.*

Price Guide: (euro)
single €105–€270
double/twin €210–€350
suite €300–€395
weekly €700–€900

Awards/Recognition: Condé Nast Johansens Best Value for Money 2010; 2 AA Rosettes 2012-2013

Location: N59, 37 miles; Galway, 40 miles; Knock Airport, 2 hour drive

Attractions: Connemara National Park; Stud Farm; Delightful Gardens and Garden School; Aran and Inish Boffin Islands; Kylemore Abbey Victorian Walled Gardens

The g Hotel

WELLPARK, GALWAY, CO GALWAY
Tel: 00 353 91 865 200
Web: www.condenastjohansens.com/theghotel **E-mail:** reservetheg@theg.ie

Our inspector loved: *The "wow" factor in every aspect of this impressive hotel and spa.*

Price Guide: (euro)
single from €125
double from €140
suite from €300

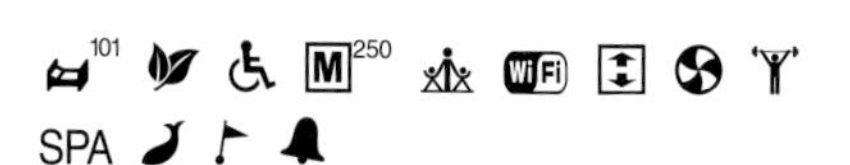

Awards/Recognition: Top 3 Hotels in the World for Design & Ambience, Condé Nast Traveller Gold List 2009; "Best Chef in Galway" Irish Restaurant Awards 2010 and 2012

Location: City Centre, 0.6 miles; Shannon Airport, 1-hour drive; Knock Airport, 75-min drive; Dublin Airport, 2-hour drive

Attractions: Spanish Arch; Galway Cathedral; Connemara National Park; Cliffs of Moher; Aran Islands

Located in the heart of Galway, The g is a 5-star luxury hotel that effortlessly combines the best of traditional Irish hospitality with stunning contemporary design, offering you a truly unforgettable experience. The hotel's glamorous interiors were created by remarkable milliner, Philip Treacy, with an emphasis on harmonious opulence that is inspired by the landscape and seashores of Galway. Make time to visit the spa, which is situated over 2 floors of the hotel and offers a wide range of ESPA treatments within a distinctively relaxing space that is simply perfect for pampering and indulging yourself. However, you may never want to leave your beautiful bedroom! Each is spacious, comfortable and has amazing cutting-edge in-room entertainment. Delicious Irish cuisine is cooked to perfection and served in a dazzling dining room, Restaurant gigi's, that combines lavish purple velvet banqueting with jewel-coloured Andrew Martin chairs.

Cahernane House Hotel

MUCKROSS ROAD, KILLARNEY, CO KERRY
Tel: 00 353 64 6631895
Web: www.condenastjohansens.com/cahernane **E-mail:** info@cahernane.com

Our inspector loved: *The sense of feeling "at home" the minute you step through the door. Irish hospitality at its very best!*

Price Guide: (euro)
single from €90
double from €130
suite from €200

Awards/Recognition: 2 AA Rosette 2012-2013

Location: Killarney, 1 mile; Kerry Airport, 14 miles

Attractions: Ring of Kerry; Muckross House; Killarney Golf Club; Killarney National Park

A shady tunnel of greenery frames the ¼ mile-long drive to this welcoming house that dates back to the 17th century, where time seems to move at a wonderfully sedate pace. The former home to the Earls of Pembroke, it stands in gorgeous parklands on the edge of Killarney's National Park, Co Kerry. You'll find that the Browne family pride themselves on their hospitality and will be keen to ensure you make the most of your stay. Bedrooms have plenty of individual personality and the suites are enhanced with beautiful antiques. Recipient of numerous awards, Herbert Room restaurant offers menus by Chef David Norris, or you can eat more informally in the Cellar Bar, home to an impressive stock of wines. There's tennis and croquet or simply enjoy garden walks and views of the National Parks untamed beauty.

ASHFORD CASTLE

CONG, CO MAYO
Tel: 00 353 94 95 46003
Web: www.condenastjohansens.com/ashfordcastle **E-mail:** ashford@ashford.ie

Our inspector loved: *The "wow" factor on arrival and the wonderful staff whose welcoming smiles are as wide as the stunning views!*

Price Guide: (euro, room only)
single/twin/double from €175
stateroom/suite from €450

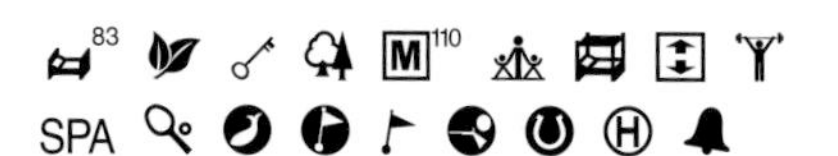

Awards/Recognition: Condé Nast Traveller Readers' Choice, Number 1 Resort Hotel in Europe 2010

Location: N84, 5 miles; Galway City, 26 miles; Galway Airport, 27 miles; Shannon Airport, 77 miles; Dublin Airport, 157 miles

Attractions: Connemara Loop; Connemara National Park; Westport: Ceidhe Fields; Leenane

This 13th-century castle stands within 350 acres of stunning estate and is the former home of Lord Ardilaun and the Guinness family. It became a luxurious hotel in 1939 and is now a veritable playground for fishing, nature and golf enthusiasts. Food lovers will also appreciate the exceptional cuisine. The Chef's creativity and inspirational use of local, seasonal and organic ingredients offer a range of dining options to suit all occasions. Choose from the 5-course table d'hôte evening menu in the George V restaurant, adorned with 11 Waterford crystal chandeliers, or the informal bistro-style à la carte menu at Cullen's. A daily snack menu is served in the Drawing Room and a 24-hour in-room dining service is also available. Relax after dinner to nightly entertainment, and enjoy the activities and facilities including falconry, horse riding, the Orvis endorsed Fly Fishing School, clay pigeon shooting, health centre and treatment rooms. Boat trips can be arranged on Lough Corrib.

Knockranny House Hotel & Spa

WESTPORT, CO MAYO
Tel: 00 353 98 28600
Web: www.condenastjohansens.com/knockranny **E-mail:** info@khh.ie

Rising into view against Croagh Patrick Mountain, this Victorian house with luxury spa evokes an image of a bygone era. Set in secluded grounds in Westport, Co Mayo, Knockranny is comfortable and welcoming. With a reputation as one of Ireland's finest hotels since 1997, you have a wide choice of bedrooms with courtyard or mountain views including Grand De Luxe, De Luxe, Master Suites and Executive Suites. Rooms are very spacious and boast king-size beds, 32" LCD TVs, surround-sound systems, free WiFi internet access, oversized bathrooms with spa bath as standard. Antique furniture features throughout the hotel and the conservatory and library look out onto magnificent scenery. You can enjoy contemporary Irish cuisine and fish dishes in the restaurant. Spa Salveo features a vitality pool, a serail mud chamber and 12 treatment rooms.

***Our inspector loved:** The superb service, delicious menus, highly commended wine list and spa!*

Price Guide: (euro)
single from €105
double/twin from €140
suite from €210

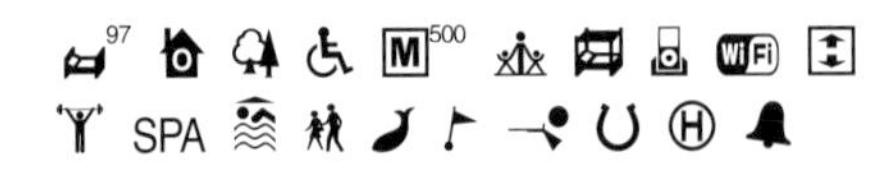

Awards/Recognition: Condé Nast Johansens/ Champagne Taittinger Wine List Award 2011; 2 AA Rosettes 2012-2013; "La Fougere"' Best Restaurant in Connaught 2011; Head Chef Seamus Commons, Best Chef in Connaught 2012

Location: Just off the N5; Town Centre 10-min walk; Train and Bus Station 15-min walk; Knock Airport, 45-min drive

Attractions: Westport House Estate; Great Western Greenway Cycle and Walkway: Croagh Patrick Mountain; Clewbay and Clare Island

SEAFIELD GOLF & SPA HOTEL

BALLYMONEY, GOREY, CO WEXFORD
Tel: 00 353 53 9424000
Web: www.condenastjohansens.com/seafieldhotel **E-mail:** sales@seafieldhotel.com

Our inspector loved: *The contemporary style, traditional service values, thermal spa and the abundance of space.*

Price Guide: (euro)
single €120
double €180
suite €525

Location: Dublin International Airport, 60 miles; Close to N11, Dublin to Wexford

Attractions: 12th-Century City of Kilkenny, Castle and Cathedral; County Wicklow, "The Garden of Ireland"; Medieval Site of Glendalough; The Coast

Style and luxury are key at Seafield, as is the warm Irish welcome it extends to each guest. Surrounded by 160 tranquil acres, this golf and spa hotel sits on the Ballymoney shore, just 1 hour from Dublin. Italian architect Francesco Beia has designed its clean, contemporary interiors to fully make the most of the views and light. Choose a Deluxe Room and enjoy sumptuous mattresses and crisp linens or indulge in an Executive Suite with balcony, walk-in shower and elegant furnishings. Families are fully catered for in exceptional Family Suites adjacent to the main hotel, and a kids' club offers evening entertainment. Private nature tours through woodland paths and onto the beach are also available for daytime adventures. More adult pursuits can be found at the 18-hole clifftop golf course, created to the highest specifications, while the award-winning Oceo Spa with its thermal suite, ice grotto and hydrotherapy pool is truly world class.

The Ritz-Carlton, Powerscourt

POWERSCOURT ESTATE, ENNISKERRY, CO WICKLOW
Tel: 00 353 1 274 8888
Web: www.condenastjohansens.com/ritzcarlton **E-mail:** powerscourtreservations@ritzcarlton.com

Surrounded by the serene woodlands, gentle green hills and sparkling lakes of Powerscourt Estate, with glorious views of the County Wicklow countryside, this sumptuous country estate beckons with an irresistible blend of luxurious country living and impeccable service, and yet cosmopolitan Dublin is only half an hour away. The bedrooms and suites are generously sized and decorated in a casually elegant style; many offer floor-to-ceiling windows, panoramic views and terraces. Dining is a delight: choose between Gordon Ramsay at Powerscourt, where the professional team creates culinary delights and the more casual Sugar Loaf Lounge, which also houses a welcoming bar. For ultimate relaxation, the peaceful ESPA treats guests to absolute luxury with 21 treatment rooms, a 20-metre Swarovski crystal-lit pool, fitness suite and state-of-the-art thermal suite. The stunning 36-hole championship golf complex is located only a few steps from the hotel.

Our inspector loved: *The "nothing is too difficult" attitude, stunning spa and the Gordon Ramsey at Powerscourt.*

Price Guide: (euro, excluding breakfast)
deluxe from €280
superior from €310
classic suite from €320
mountain view suite from €340

Location: Dublin Airport, 35-min drive; Dublin City Centre, 30-min drive; Glendalough, 40-min drive; Dun Laoghaire Ferry Port, 25-min drive

Attractions: Powerscourt House and Gardens; Glendalough; Dublin City Centre; Trinity College

Sir George Fistonich, Auckland, New Zealand circa 1960
26
26
VILLA MARIA
NEW ZEALAND
SAUVIGNON BLANC
CELEBRATING
50
YEARS
of exceptional winemaking
New Zealand's most
awarded winery
Villa Maria Estate was founded 50 years ago
by Sir George Fistonich. Still proudly family
owned, Villa Maria is recognised as an icon
in the New Zealand wine industry, producing
wines of exceptional quality.
VILLA MARIA
VILLA MARIA ESTATE
New Zealand's Most Awarded Winery
Hatch Mansfield is the exclusive UK agent for Villa Maria wines
For more information please visit: www.villamariaestate.co.uk
Telephone 01344 871800 · email info@hatch.co.uk

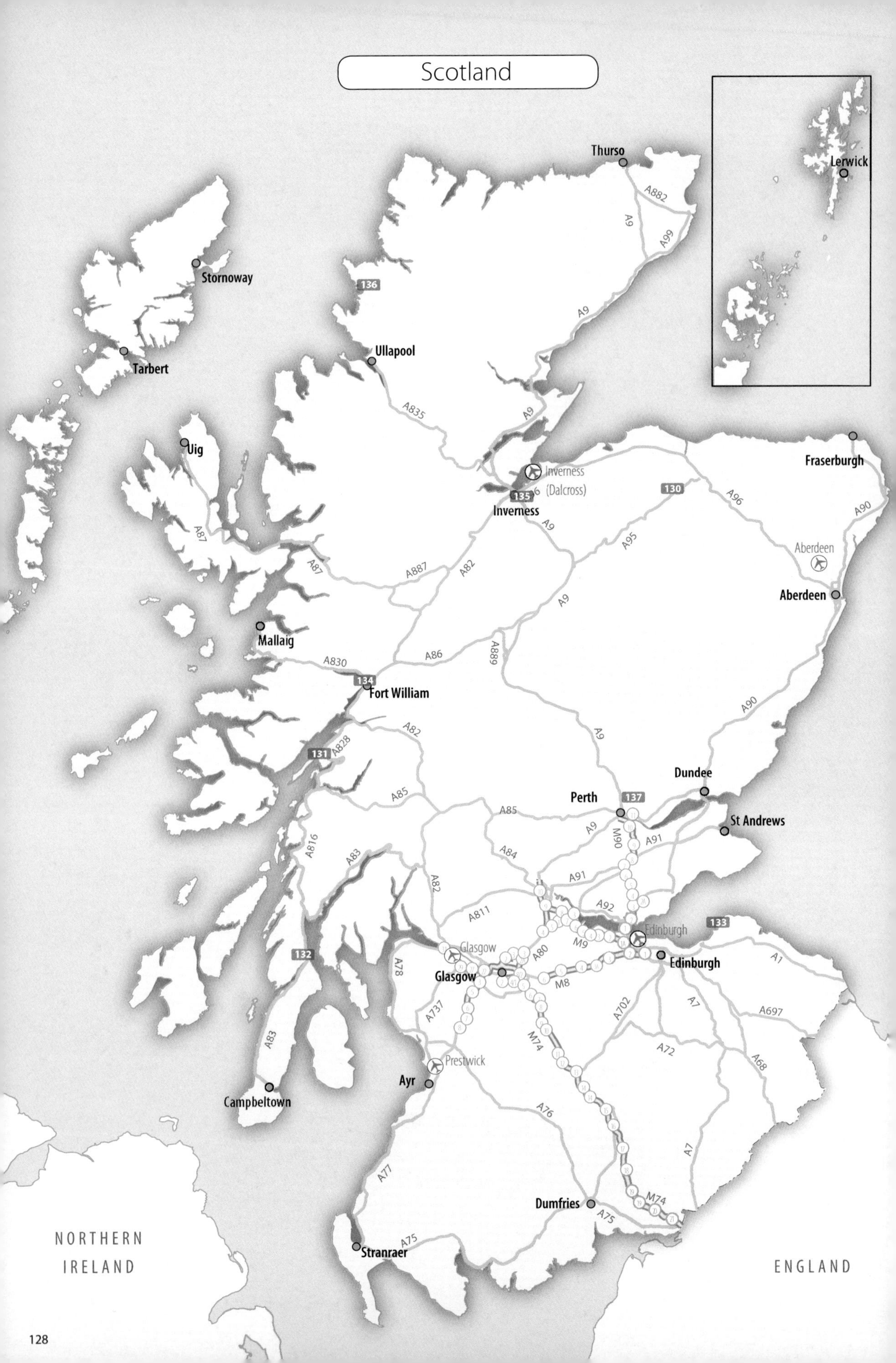

Scotland
Thurso
A882
A9
A99
Lerwick
Stornoway
136
Ullapool
Tarbert
A835
Uig
Inverness
(Dalcross)
135
Inverness
130
A96
A90
Fraserburgh
A87
A887
A82
A95
Aberdeen
Aberdeen
Mallaig
A830
A86
A889
134
Fort William
A82
A90
131
A828
A85
Dundee
Perth
137
A85
St Andrews
A816
A83
A84
M90
A91
A82
A91
A811
A92
Edinburgh
133
Glasgow
M9
Edinburgh
A78
Glasgow
M8
A1
A737
A702
A7
A697
M74
A72
A83
Prestwick
A68
Ayr
Campbeltown
A76
A7
A77
Dumfries
M74
A75
A75
Stranraer
NORTHERN
IRELAND
ENGLAND

Scotland

Airds Hotel, Argyll & Bute, Scotland - p131

For further information on Scotland, please contact:

Visit Scotland
Ocean Point One
94 Ocean Drive
Edinburgh EH6 6JH
Tel: 0845 859 1006
E-mail: info@visitscotland.com
www.visitscotland.com

Edinburgh & Lothians Tourist Board
www.edinburgh.org

Highlands of Scotland
www.visithighlands.com

Visit Scottish Borders
Tel: 0845 2255 121
www.visitscottishborders.com

Loganair
Tel: +44 (0)141 8487594
www.loganair.co.uk

Flybe
Tel: 0871 700 2000
www.flybe.com

or see **pages 155-158** for details of local historic houses, castles and gardens to visit during your stay.

For additional places to stay in Scotland turn to **pages 149-153** where a listing of our Recommended Small Hotels, Inns & Restaurants Guide can be found.

Craigellachie Hotel of Speyside

CRAIGELLACHIE, ABERLOUR, BANFFSHIRE AB38 9SR
Tel: 01340 881204 **International:** +44 (0)1340 881204
Web: www.condenastjohansens.com/craigellachie **E-mail:** generalmanager.craigellachie@ohiml.com

Our inspector loved: *The new public bar area, which gives a local feel to this country hotel.*

Price Guide:
single £80–£120
double/twin £95–£135
four poster £125–£165

Awards/Recognition: 1 AA Rosette 2012-2013

Location: Just off the A95; A9, 38 miles; Inverness Airport, 43 miles; Elgin Train Station, 10 miles

Attractions: Whisky Trail; Fishing on River Spey; Beaches at Lossiemouth; Culloden

You can be sure of a warm Highland welcome at Craigellachie, a grand country hotel within spectacular surroundings. Located where the Fiddich and Spey Rivers meet at Aberlour, this an ideal spot for angling enthusiasts to land some of the world's best wild salmon due to its fast flowing current. Uninterrupted views over this breathtaking countryside are simply awe-inspiring, and for those of you in search of active pursuits, there are many to choose from. At the end of the day, there will be a inviting lounge complete with roaring log fire waiting for you or in the bar an impressive stock of over 700 whiskies can be discussed with the hotel's own specialist. Fine Scottish cuisine with an emphasis on seasonal and local produce is served in the Ben Aigan Restaurant.

AIRDS HOTEL

PORT APPIN, APPIN, ARGYLL PA38 4DF
Tel: 01631 730236 **International:** +44 (0)1631 730236
Web: www.condenastjohansens.com/airdshotel **E-mail:** airds@airds-hotel.com

Our inspector loved: *The elegant and luxurious fusion of the old and the new, which works extremely well.*

Price Guide: (including dinner)
standard £275–£315
superior £315–£408
suite £370–£490

Awards/Recognition: Relais & Châteaux; 3 AA Rosettes 2011-2012; 3 Stars Sustainable Restaurant Association; Eat Scotland Gold Award

Location: Oban, 20 miles; Fort William, 27 miles; Glasgow Airport, 135-min drive; Edinburgh Airport, 165-min drive

Attractions: Ben Nevis and Gondola; Oban Whisky Distillery; Glencoe; Arduaine Gardens

Capturing the essence of the romantic retreat, Airds Hotel is a family-run luxury hotel and gourmet restaurant. Once an 18th-century ferry inn, its atmosphere is relaxed and elegant with intimate yet attentive service and its setting on the west coast of Scotland makes the most of the undulating coastline that surrounds the Appin Peninsula. The 8 bedrooms and 3 suites are warm and inviting, and vary in style from "country house" to more contemporary. Crisp Frette linens, complimentary newspapers and Bulgari toiletries add thoughtful touches, while Vi Spring beds guarantee you a good night's sleep. Some rooms feature spectacular views across Loch Linnhe and the Morvern Mountains. Reputed to be one of the best in Scotland, the inspiring restaurant led by Fellow Master Chef of Great Britain Robert MacPherson, serves an abundance of fresh ingredients from locally sourced fish and seafood to roast fillet of Scotch beef.

Stonefield Castle

TARBERT, LOCH FYNE, ARGYLL PA29 6YJ
Tel: 01880 820836 **International:** +44 (0)1880 820836
Web: www.condenastjohansens.com/stonefield **E-mail:** generalmanager.stonefieldcastle@ohiml.com

Discover the stunning 4-star Baronial Stonefield Castle near the pretty village of Tarbert on the Mull of Kintyre. Overlooking the beautiful Loch Fyne, this classic example of an elegant Victorian house stands within 60 acres of woodlands rich in azaleas and rhododrendons. The scenery in the area is quite breathtaking. Vast fireplaces, richly decorated ceilings and beautiful wood panelling have been carefully restored and now provide a stunning setting that is complemented by a warm and welcoming atmosphere that greets each guest. The dining room has some simply staggering views that look right out to sea and is the ideal setting to enjoy some of the fantastic selection of locally sourced produce that is found within the estate.

Our inspector loved: *The outstanding collection of rhododendrons and azaleas, which complement this imposing old building.*

Price Guide: (including dinner)
single from £140
double £180-£235
suite from £225

Awards/Recognition: 1 AA Rosette 2012-2013

Location: Glasgow Airport, 2-hour drive; Lochgilphead, 11 miles; Oban, 45 miles; Campbeltown, 45 miles

Attractions: Inveraray Castle and Jail; Islands of Islay, Arran and Gigha and Their Distilleries; Crarae Gardens

Greywalls and Chez Roux

MUIRFIELD, GULLANE, EAST LOTHIAN EH31 2EG
Tel: 01620 842 144 **International:** +44 (0)1620 842 144
Web: www.condenastjohansens.com/greywalls **E-mail:** enquiries@greywalls.co.uk

Our inspector loved: *Enjoying lunch in a secluded area of the breathtakingly beautiful gardens.*

Price Guide:
single £80-£300
double £230-£320
colonel's house from £1,235

Location: Edinburgh City, 30-min drive; A1, 15 miles; Edinburgh Airport, 45-min drive

Attractions: Muirfield Golf Course; Beaches; Edinburgh Castle; Tantallon Castle; Glenkinchie Distillery

You'll find the elegance and warm Scottish charm of this impressive Edwardian hotel quite captivating. A relaxed retreat set in 6 acres of walled gardens on the very edge of the historic Muirfield championship golf course, Greywalls has hosted the British Open no less than 12 times. Golf enthusiasts will never want to leave this green paradise, where 10 more challenging courses are located within 5 miles of the hotel. Homely and gracefully stylish, filled with wonderful fabrics and fine antique furniture, the guest rooms are peaceful havens. An additional 4 bedrooms are located in the nearby self-catering Colonel's House; an ideal setting for a family holiday or golfing group of up to 8. The superb cuisine is overseen by Chef Albert Roux OBE, KFO head of the famous cooking dynasty behind such establishments as Le Gavroche, which was the first ever restaurant in the UK to be awarded 3 Michelin Stars. Managed by Inverlochy Castle Management International.

Inverlochy Castle

TORLUNDY, FORT WILLIAM PH33 6SN

Tel: 01397 702177 **International:** +44 (0)1397 702177

Web: www.condenastjohansens.com/inverlochy **E-mail:** info@inverlochy.co.uk

***Our inspector loved:** The romantic setting and "wow" factor of this handsome castle!*

Price Guide:
single £265-£375
double £320-£525
superior £440-£550
suite £480-£695

Queen Victoria's words from 1873, "I never saw a lovelier or more romantic spot," describe Inverlochy perfectly, and the first Lord Abinger who built the castle in 1863 certainly knew how to pick a gorgeous location in the foothills of Ben Nevis. Today, the castle makes a splendid hotel managed by Jane Watson and first impressions of the massive reception room featuring Venetian crystal chandeliers, a Michaelangelo-style ceiling and a handsome staircase leading to 3 elaborately decorated dining rooms, carry a real "wow" factor. Bedrooms are spacious, individually furnished and offer every comfort. Michelin-Starred chef Philip Carnegie, creates modern British cuisine using local game, hand picked wild mushrooms and scallops from the Isle of Skye. Various outdoor activities await you and stunning historical landscapes are nearby. Managed by Inverlochy Castle Management International.

Awards/Recognition: 1 Star Michelin 2012; 3 AA Rosettes 2012-2013; Relais & Châteaux

Location: On A82; Fort William Railway Station, 4 miles; Inverness Airport, 69 miles; Glasgow Airport, 105 miles

Attractions: Ben Nevis; Glencoe; Glenfinnan; Loch Ness; The Jacobite Steam Train - aka Hogwarts Express for all Harry Potter fans

Rocpool Reserve and Chez Roux

CULDUTHEL ROAD, INVERNESS, IV2 4AG
Tel: 01463 240089 **International:** +44 (0)1463 240089
Web: www.condenastjohansens.com/rocpool **E-mail:** info@rocpool.com

Our inspector loved: *The stunning views over the city from the top-floor bedroom's outside hot tub.*

Price Guide:
hip (single) £150-£175
hip £185-£210
chic £215-£260
decadent £265-£315
extra decadent £320-£395

Awards/Recognition: Condé Nast Johansens Most Excellent City Hotel 2011; Scottish Restaurant Awards Best Newcomer Restaurant 2010

Location: City Centre, 5-min walk; Inverness Airport, 10 miles

Attractions: Castle Stuart Golf Course; Loch Ness and Caledonian Canal; Culloden Battlefield

Expect to be bowled over by Rocpool Reserve, a boutique hotel overlooking Inverness's riverside. Elegant and contemporary design harmoniously combines with classical elements, and superb staff offer first-class service with phenomenal attention to detail. The décor follows a colour scheme of red, black and white, and bedrooms are fitted with plasma TVs, DVD players, iPod docking stations and luxuries such as Egyptian linens, king-size beds and Italian ceramics in bathrooms; 2 rooms have a hot tub on the terrace! Unwind at the bar during cocktail hour before dining in Chez Roux. Overlooking the river it serves local Scottish produce blended with classic French country cuisine, all overseen by multi award-winning Chef Albert Roux OBE, KFO head of the famous cooking dynasty behind such establishments as Le Gavroche, which was the first ever restaurant in the UK to be awarded 3 Michelin Stars. Managed by Inverlochy Castle Management International.

Inver Lodge Hotel and Chez Roux

LOCHINVER, SUTHERLAND IV27 4LU

Tel: 01571 844496 **International:** +44 (0)1571 844496

Web: www.condenastjohansens.com/inverlodge **E-mail:** stay@inverlodge.com

Our inspector loved: *The sparkling welcome, wonderful hospitality and superior housekeeping.*

Price Guide:
single £115–£150
double £215–£265
suite £320–£480

Location: Inverness Airport and Station, 2-hour drive; Lairg Railway Station, 1-hour drive

Attractions: Wild Unspoilt Scenery; Fishing on Lochs and Rivers; Bird-watching

Prepare to be stunned by Inver Lodge, a charming 5-star hotel and haven of peace and tranquillity for those seeking a family break or romantic weekend enveloped by nature. From a hilltop perch, Inver Lodge looks down onto the quiet fishing village of Lochinver and across the waters of the loch to the distant Western Isles. Moorland reaches to the hotel doorway, red deer graze outside the windows, Atlantic seals pop up in the harbour and golden eagles soar over the mountains! Relax, chat and drink in the welcoming foyer lounge before sampling "hearty country cooking" at the exceptional Chez Roux restaurant, now overseen by famed Chef Albert Roux OBE, KFO head of the famous cooking dynasty behind such establishments as Le Gavroche, which was the first restaurant in the UK to be awarded 3 Michelin Stars. Then retire to your delightfully comfortable bedroom and admire the spectacular sea view. Managed by Inverlochy Castle Management International.

The Murrayshall House Hotel & Golf Courses

SCONE, PERTH, PERTHSHIRE PH2 7PH
Tel: 01738 551171 **International:** +44 (0)1738 551171
Web: www.condenastjohansens.com/murrayshall **E-mail:** info@murrayshall.com

Our inspector loved: *The combination of old country estate ambience with 21st-century modern comforts.*

Price Guide: (per person)
single £120
double £80
suite £95

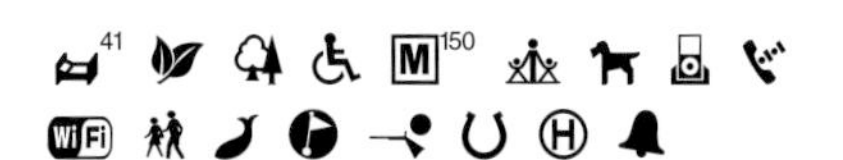

Awards/Recognition: 2 AA Rosettes 2012-2013; Eat Scotland Silver Award 2012

Location: Perth City, 3 miles; Perth Airport (Small Aircrafts Only), 2 miles; M90, 4 miles; Edinburgh, 50-min drive

Attractions: Scone Palace; Glamis Castle; Scone Racecourse; Golf at St Andrews, Gleneagles and Carnoustie

A golfer's paradise, this 350-acre private estate is home to two 18-hole golf courses in stunning Perthshire countryside. The perfect escape from the hustle and bustle of modern life, this elegant Victorian country home is welcoming and relaxed with individually appointed bedrooms and suites offering a unique blend of tradition and modern day comfort. Start the day with fresh free-range eggs, locally cured bacon and kippers, and return for dinner in either the informal Club Bar & Restaurant or the traditional Old Masters restaurant where the award-winning chef creates authentic Scottish favourites with a twist. A day wouldn't be complete without a game of golf - buggies are available - or a walk along the numerous paths meandering through the estate and nearby countryside. Other leisure pursuits include horse riding at the famous nearby Gleneagles Equestrian Centre, cycling and adrenaline-fuelled quad biking and off-roading.

Wales
Holyhead
A55
142
Llandudno
A55
A55
A5
Caernarfon
A470
143
A487
Snowdonia
National Park
A5
A494
A483
A534
Wrexham
A5
A494
A470
146
Dolgellau
144
A458
A487
A470
A470
A483
A44
A470
A483
140
Aberystwyth
ENGLAND
A487
A470
A44
A44
A483
141
A483
A487
147
A483
A470
A438
Fishguard
Brecon
A40
A40
A479
Carmarthen
A40
A470
A40
A40
145
A477
A48
A483
Brecon Beacons National Park
Abergavenny
A40
Pembroke
Swansea
M4
A465
A449
M4
M4
A470
Cardiff
Cardiff

Wales

Nanteos Mansion, Ceredigion, Wales – p140

For further information on Wales, please contact:

Wales Tourist Board
Tel: 08708 300 306
E-mail: info@visitwales.co.uk
www.visitwales.co.uk

North Wales Tourism
Tel: 01492 531731
E-mail: croeso@nwt.co.uk
www.nwt.co.uk

Mid Wales Tourism
Tel: 01654 702653
E-mail: info@midwalestourism.co.uk
www.visitmidwales.co.uk

South Wales Tourism
www.visitsouthwales.com

South West Wales Tourism Partnership
Tel: +44 (0)1558 669091
www.swwtp.co.uk

Cadw: Welsh Historic Monuments
Tel: +44 (0)1443 33 6000
E-mail: cadw@wales.gsi.gov.uk
www.cadw.wales.gov.uk

Millennium Stadium
Tel: 08442 777 888
E-mail: info@ millenniumstadium.com
www.millenniumstadium.com

or see **pages 155-158** for details of local historic houses, castles and gardens to visit during your stay.

For additional places to stay in Wales turn to **pages 149-153** where a listing of our Recommended Small Hotels, Inns & Restaurants Guide can be found.

Nanteos Mansion

RHYDYFELIN, ABERYSTWYTH, CEREDIGION SY23 4LU
Tel: 01970 600522 **International:** +44 (0)1970 600522
Web: www.condenastjohansens.com/nanteos **E-mail:** info@nanteos.com

The re-invention of Nanteos Mansion from private home, open house and restaurant to luxury country house hotel is now complete. A remarkable investment of over £4.5 million has transformed the property to its grandeur and the refurbishment thoughtfully continues with plans for leisure facilities including a spa. Every care has been taken to maintain its elegant 18th-century charm whilst incorporating glamorous designs, contemporary amenities and 5-star hotel services. The newly opened Nightingale Restaurant presents refined menus of locally sourced produce, and afternoon tea, morning coffee and light lunches can be taken in The Library or Morning Room. Guests can choose to stay in one of the sumptuous Mansion guest rooms or hire the nearby 4-bedroomed cottage for a self-catering break or fully-serviced, exceptionally private getaway. In fact, the entire estate can be exclusively hired for weddings, meetings, product launches or film/photo shoots.

Our inspector loved: *The luxurious bedrooms of this majestic country house.*

Price Guide:
single £90
double £150
suite £180-£220

Location: B4340, 1 mile; A487, 2 miles; Aberystwyth, 2 miles; Aberystwyth Train Station, 2 miles

Attractions: Welsh Coast and National Trust Beaches; Devils Bridge Falls and Nature Trail; The Hafod Estate; Llanerchaeron (National Trust)

THE FALCONDALE

FALCONDALE DRIVE, LAMPETER, CEREDIGION SA48 7RX
Tel: 01570 422910 **International:** +44 (0)1570 422910
Web: www.condenastjohansens.com/falcondale **E-mail:** info@thefalcondale.co.uk

Our inspector loved: *The attentive service at this friendly hotel set in beautiful gardens and grounds.*

Price Guide:
single from £99
double/twin £139–£195

Awards/Recognition: 2 AA Rosettes 2012-2013

Location: A485, 1 mile; A40, 10 miles; Cardiff Airport, 95 miles; M4, 30 miles

Attractions: Llanerchaeron (National Trust); Dolaucothi Gold Mines (National Trust); University of Wales; National Botanic Garden of Wales

This Victorian Italian-style villa in the heart of Wales is a welcoming country escape set in 14 peaceful acres of ornamental woods and lawns with the stunning backdrop of the Cambrian Mountains and Cardigan Bay. A family-run property available for exclusive use, its wide range of guest rooms include Small and Standard rooms which are perfect for those travelling on business or visiting for a short break. Reserve a Better or Best room to enjoy the fabulous views over the Teifi Valley. Food at the award-winning restaurant is seriously good and has gained a reputation for getting the best out of the region's rich larder: lobster, crab, Welsh lamb and beef, as well as speciality cheeses often appear on the inspiring seasonal menus. The Falcondale organises various themed packages throughout the year such as Romantic Getaways and Dog Training courses so be sure to enquire about the latest offers when booking.

St Tudno Hotel & Restaurant

NORTH PROMENADE, LLANDUDNO, NORTH WALES LL30 2LP
Tel: 01492 874411 **International:** +44 (0)1492 874411
Web: www.condenastjohansens.com/sttudno **E-mail:** sttudnohotel@btinternet.com

Our inspector loved: *The warm welcome and friendly staff at this charming sea front hotel.*

Price Guide:
single from £75
double/twin £98–£220
suite £260–£310

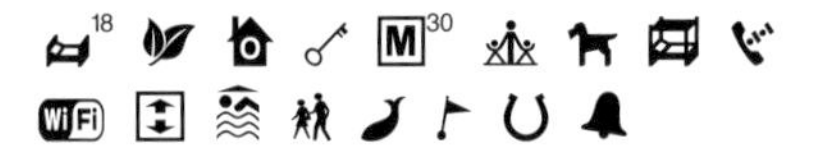

Awards/Recognition: 2 AA Rosettes 2012-2013

Location: On the A470; A55, 4 miles; Chester, 45 miles; Manchester Airport, 65 miles

Attractions: Theatre at Llandudno; Bodnant Gardens; Dry Ski Slope and Tobaggan Run on the Great Orme; Conwy and Caernarfon Castles

Undoubtedly one of the most delightful small hotels in Wales and indeed to be found on the coast of Britain, St Tudno has just celebrated its 40th year and offers a very special experience. A former winner of the Johansen's Hotel of the Year Award for Excellence, this elegantly and lovingly refurbished hotel provides a particularly warm welcome from Martin Bland and his staff. The individually designed bedrooms have many thoughtful extras and the Terrace Restaurant is regarded as one of Wales' leading places to eat. A little oasis at this town house is the indoor heated swimming pool and secret garden. The St Tudno has won a host of awards: Best Seaside Resort Hotel in Great Britain (Good Hotel Guide), Welsh Hotel of the Year, 2 major wine awards and even an accolade for having the Best Hotel Loos in Britain. Ideally situated for visits to Snowdonia National Park, world-famous Bodnant Gardens, Anglesey and glorious walks on the Great Orme.

RUTHIN CASTLE HOTEL & SPA

RUTHIN, DENBIGHSHIRE LL15 2NU
Tel: 01824 702664 **International:** +44 (0)1824 702664
Web: www.condenastjohansens.com/ruthincastle **E-mail:** reception@ruthincastle.co.uk

Our inspector loved: *The recently refurbished bedrooms at this historic Welsh Castle.*

Price Guide:
single from £80
double £99-£225
suite £225-£330

Awards/Recognition: 2 AA Rosettes 2012-2013

Location: A525, 0.5 miles; A55, 8 miles; Chester, 22 miles; Conwy, 23 miles

Attractions: Snowdonia National Park; Historic City of Chester; North Wales Coast; Clwyd Hills

In gorgeous Welsh countryside close to Chester lies the magical Ruthin Castle amidst acres of peaceful woods, parkland and gardens. This romantic castle has a rich, royal 700-year heritage including ownership by King Edward I, Henry VIII and Elizabeth I. It is now a warm, welcoming hotel with individually styled bedrooms including themed Royal Salons and Sovereign Suites. Lounges feature cosy open fires, and Bertie's award-winning dining room presents imaginative cuisine created from Welsh ingredients. Enjoy evening entertainment showcasing Welsh culture at Jesters Feast medieval themed banquets in the Great Hall and indulge yourself at The Moat spa. The hotel's extraordinary spa partly resides within the rustic woodlands of the ancient castle's moat and represents a new concept in social spa experiences drawing on the majestic North Wales setting in its design and unique use of quality Welsh products.

Penmaenuchaf Hall

PENMAENPOOL, DOLGELLAU, GWYNEDD LL40 1YB
Tel: 01341 422129 **International:** +44 (0)1341 422129
Web: www.condenastjohansens.com/penmaenuchafhall **E-mail:** relax@penhall.co.uk

Our inspector loved: *The owners' care and attention to their guests. This is an award-winning hotel with beautiful gardens.*

Price Guide:
single £115–£180
double/twin £170–£270

From the moment you've climbed the long tree-lined driveway, you'll relax and enjoy this glorious setting. Nestled near Dolgellau in the Snowdonia National Park, this award-winning hotel offers stunning views across the Mawddach Estuary to distant wooded mountain slopes. The Hall is a Victorian build maintaining its original oak and mahogany panelling, stained-glass windows, slate floors and log fires in winter. The 21-acre grounds blend lawns, both a water and lavender garden and woodland. Guests can enjoy bedrooms showcasing fabulous balconies and the Garden Room restaurant, where food lovers can dine on imaginative, seasonal dishes. Spend your break fishing along 10 miles of the Mawddach River or the "llyn Penmaenuchaf" within the hotel's grounds, mountain biking, visiting sandy beaches and playing championship golf courses. Penmaenuchaf Hall won the AA Hotel of the Year Wales 2011 and the Visit Wales Gold Award 2011-2012.

Awards/Recognition: Condé Nast Johansens Most Excellent Country House Hotel 2011; Condé Nast Johansens and Champagne Taittinger Wine List Awards, Special Commendation - Education of the Customer 2011; 1 AA Rosette 2012-2013

Location: A493, 0.5 miles; A470, 1.5 miles; Shrewsbury, 60 miles; Chester, 60 miles

Attractions: Snowdonia National Park; Narrow Guage Railways; Bodnant Garden; Portmeirion

THE GROVE HOTEL

MOLLESTON, NARBERTH, PEMBROKESHIRE SA67 8BX
Tel: 01834 860 915 **International:** +44 (0)1834 860 915
Web: www.condenastjohansens.com/grovenarberth **E-mail:** info@thegrove-narberth.co.uk

Our inspector loved: *The great attention to detail, excellent food and beautifully furnished, individual rooms.*

Price Guide:
single £140-£280
double £150-£290

Awards/Recognition: Condé Nast Johansens Taittinger Wine List Award, Best Newcomer 2012; 2 AA Rosettes 2012-2013

Location: A4115, 1.3 miles; A478, 2 miles; A40, 10 miles; Tenby, 10 miles

Attractions: Pembrokeshire Coastal National Park and Beaches; St Davids and its Cathedral; Skomer Island; National Botanical Gardens of Wales

Nestled amidst the rolling hills of beautiful Pembrokeshire and with breathtaking views of the Preseli Mountains, this charming 18th-century country house is impressive both inside and out. One of the most intimate and unique luxury hotels in Wales, and steeped in history, The Grove Hotel offers 14 individually designed guest rooms and 6 characterful suites surrounded by 26 acres of scenic grounds. Each bedroom and suite is filled with luxurious Zoffany and Melin Tregwynt furnishings and displays beautiful local and international artwork. Guests in need of serious pampering will love the deep cast-iron baths, underfloor heating and wonderful in-room aromatherapy massages. The restaurant presents a truly sumptuous dining experience, serving modern British food creatively prepared from seasonal and locally sourced ingredients.

Lake Vyrnwy Hotel & Spa

LAKE VYRNWY, LLANWDDYN, POWYS SY10 0LY
Tel: 01691 870 692 **International:** +44 (0)1691 870 692
Web: www.condenastjohansens.com/lakevyrnwy **E-mail:** info@lakevyrnwyhotel.co.uk

The location of Lake Vyrnwy Hotel & Spa is just magical, overlooking the stunning lake surrounded by wild moorland, forest and the rugged Berwyn Mountains. A picturesque getaway enveloped by walking trails and opportunities for clay shooting, fishing, water sports and cycling, this wonderful setting can be admired through the windows of the warm and inviting drawing room from sumptuous sofas and balconies located off most bedrooms. As the sun goes down, the Tower Bar's balcony is the perfect place to savour a glass of wine before enjoying dinner in the restaurant where the menus reflect a genuine enthusiasm for food and utilise as much local produce as possible. The contemporary Tavern Bar is ideal for more informal dining. Why not pamper yourself in the luxury spa and thermal suite, with its extensive range of therapies and array of facilities that include an Arabian rasul mud therapy chamber and Monsoon shower.

Our inspector loved: *Enjoying the spectacular views from the balcony of the Tavern Bar.*

Price Guide:
single £106–£211
double/twin £131–£187
premier double £208–£236

Awards/Recognition: 1 AA Rosette 2012-2013

Location: A490, 8 miles; A495, 12 miles; Shrewsbury, 35 miles; Chester, 50 miles

Attractions: Powis Castle; Snowdonia National Park; Portmeirion; Centre for Alternative Technology; Little Railways of Wales

Lake Country House & Spa

LLANGAMMARCH WELLS, POWYS LD4 4BS
Tel: 01591 620202 **International:** +44 (0)1591 620202
Web: www.condenastjohansens.com/lakecountryhouse **E-mail:** info@lakecountryhouse.co.uk

***Our inspector loved:** Relaxing in the outdoor hot tub overlooking the lake and accompanying wildlife.*

Price Guide:
single from £145
superior from £195
suite from £240

Awards/Recognition: Condé Nast Johansens Most Excellent Spa 2009; 2 AA Rosettes 2012-2013

Location: A 485, 3 miles; A 470, 8 miles; Hay on Wye, 21 miles; Cardiff Airport, 52 miles

Attractions: Brecon Beacons National Park; Cambrian Mountains and Elan Valley; Aberglasney House and Gardens; Raglan Castle

Trout leaping up from a serene lake, otters in the river, carpets of wild flowers bobbing in the breeze and badgers ambling by the woods nearby are all sights to be savoured at Lake Country House with luxury spa, surrounded by 50 acres of unspoilt land. This hidden gem is a haven for wildlife enthusiasts with over 100 bird-nesting boxes within the grounds and ample opportunities for fishing and horse riding. Feast on traditional Welsh teas by a roaring log fire in one of the decadent lounges during winter or beneath the chestnut tree during summer. Enjoy fresh produce and herbs from the garden in the restaurant and sample some of the superb wines from the list of over 300 bins. To complete your stay, why not visit the Condé Nast Johansens award-winning lakeside spa; an inspired setting to unwind and totally relax.

Preferred Partner for fine linens and towelling to Condé Nast Johansens

RICHARD HAWORTH
Est. 1876

BOUTIQUE LINEN
hotel luxury at home

Hotel Enquiries - Tel: 0870 777 5000 Web: www.richardhaworth.co.uk
Guest Enquiries - Tel: 0845 337 7732 Web: www.boutiquelinen.com
Richard Haworth Ltd, Kearsley Mill, Stoneclough, Manchester, M26 1RH, United Kingdom

Small Hotels, Inns & Restaurants - Great Britain & Ireland

Properties listed below can be found in our Recommended Small Hotels, Inns & Restaurants – Great Britain & Ireland 2013 Guide

CHANNEL ISLANDS - GUERNSEY (SARK)

La Sablonnerie

Little Sark, Sark, Guernsey GY10 1SD.

Tel: 01481 832061
www.condenastjohansens.com/lasablonnerie

CHANNEL ISLANDS - JERSEY (ROZEL BAY)

Château La Chaire

Rozel Bay, Jersey JE3 6AJ

Tel: 01534 863354
www.condenastjohansens.com/chateaulachaire

CORNWALL - LIZARD

Atlantic House

Pentreath Lane, Lizard, Cornwall TR12 7NY

Tel: 01326 290399
www.condenastjohansens.com/atlantichselizard

CUMBRIA - WINDERMERE

Applegarth Villa

College Road, Windermere, Cumbria LA23 1BU

Tel: 015394 43206
www.condenastjohansens.com/applegarth

CUMBRIA - WINDERMERE

Cedar Manor Hotel

Ambleside Road, Windermere, Cumbria LA23 1AX

Tel: 015394 43192
www.condenastjohansens.com/cedarmanor

CUMBRIA - WINDERMERE

The Windermere Suites

New Road, Windermere, Cumbria LA23 2LA

Tel: 015394 47672
www.condenastjohansens.com/windermeresuites

DERBYSHIRE - BAKEWELL (DARLEY DALE)

Holmefield Country Guest House

Dale Road North, Darley Dale, Near Bakewell, Matlock, Derbyshire DE4 2HY

Tel: 01629 735347
www.condenastjohansens.com/holmefield

DEVON - BABBACOMBE

The Cary Arms

Babbacombe Beach, South Devon TQ1 3LX

Tel: 01803 327110
www.condenastjohansens.com/caryarms

DEVON - MARTINHOE (EXMOOR NATIONAL PARK)

The Old Rectory Hotel

Martinhoe, Exmoor National Park, Devon EX31 4QT

Tel: 01598 763368
www.condenastjohansens.com/oldrectoryexmoor

DEVON - STAVERTON (NEAR TOTNES)

Kingston House

Staverton, Near Totnes, Devon TQ9 6AR

Tel: 01803 762 235
www.condenastjohansens.com/kingstonhouse

DEVON - TAVISTOCK (GULWORTHY)

The Horn of Plenty Hotel & Restaurant

Gulworthy, Tavistock, Devon PL19 8JD

Tel: 01822 832528
www.condenastjohansens.com/thehornofplenty

DORSET - SHERBORNE (OBORNE)

The Grange at Oborne

Oborne, Near Sherborne, Dorset DT9 4LA

Tel: 01935 813463
www.condenastjohansens.com/grangesherborne

GLOUCESTERSHIRE - BIBURY (COTSWOLDS)

The Swan Hotel

Bibury, Gloucestershire GL7 5NW

Tel: 01285 740695
www.condenastjohansens.com/swanhotelbibury

GLOUCESTERSHIRE - MORETON-IN-MARSH

The White Hart Royal Hotel

High Street, Moreton-in-Marsh, Gloucestershire GL56 0BA

Tel: 01608 650731
www.condenastjohansens.com/whitehartroyal

GLOUCESTERSHIRE - MORETON-IN-MARSH (BLOCKLEY)

Lower Brook House

Blockley, Nr Moreton-in-Marsh, Gloucestershire GL56 9DS

Tel: 01386 700286
www.condenastjohansens.com/lowerbrookhouse

GLOUCESTERSHIRE - NEWENT

Three Choirs Vineyards Estate

Newent, Gloucestershire GL18 1LS

Tel: 01531 890223
www.condenastjohansens.com/threechoirs

Small Hotels, Inns & Restaurants - Great Britain & Ireland

Properties listed below can be found in our Recommended Small Hotels, Inns & Restaurants – Great Britain & Ireland 2013 Guide

HAMPSHIRE - BROCKENHURST

The Pig-in the Forest

Beaulieu Road, Brockenhurst, New Forest, Hampshire SO42 7QL

Tel: 01590 622354
www.condenastjohansens.com/thepig

HAMPSHIRE - LYMINGTON (HORDLE)

The Mill At Gordleton

Silver Street, Hordle, Nr Lymington, New Forest, Hampshire SO41 6DJ

Tel: 01590 682219
www.condenastjohansens.com/themillatgordleton

HAMPSHIRE - PORTSMOUTH

Spitbank Fort

The Departure Lounge, Unit 2, The Mill, Royal Clarence Marina, Gosport, Portsmouth, Hampshire PO16 0PY

Tel: 01494 682682
www.condenastjohansens.com/spitbankfort

HEREFORDSHIRE - ROSS-ON-WYE

Wilton Court Restauant with Rooms

Wilton, Ross-on-Wye, Herefordshire HR9 6AQ

Tel: 01989 562569
www.condenastjohansens.com/wiltoncourthotel

ISLE OF WIGHT - SEAVIEW

The Priory Bay Hotel

Priory Drive, Seaview, Isle of Wight PO34 5BU

Tel: 01983 613146
www.condenastjohansens.com/priorybayiow

ISLE OF WIGHT - SHANKLIN

Rylstone Manor

Rylstone Gardens, Shanklin, Isle of Wight PO37 6RG

Tel: 01983 862806
www.condenastjohansens.com/rylstonemanor

KENT - TENTERDEN (NEAR ASHFORD)

Little Silver Country Hotel

Ashford Road, St Michaels, Tenterden, Kent TN30 6SP

Tel: 01233 850321
www.condenastjohansens.com/littlesilver

LANCASHIRE - PRESTON (LONGRIDGE)

Ferrari's Restaurant & Hotel

Thornley, Longridge, Preston, Lancashire PR3 2TB

Tel: 01772 783148
www.condenastjohansens.com/ferraris

LINCOLNSHIRE - LINCOLN

The Old Palace

Minster Yard, Lincoln, Lincolnshire LN2 1PU

Tel: 01522 580000
www.condenastjohansens.com/oldpalace

NORFOLK - NORWICH (THORPE ST ANDREW)

The Old Rectory

103 Yarmouth Road, Norwich, Norfolk NR7 0HF

Tel: 01603 700772
www.condenastjohansens.com/oldrectorynorwich

NORTHUMBERLAND - BAMBURGH

Waren House Hotel

Waren Mill, Bamburgh, Northumberland NE70 7EE

Tel: 01668 214581
www.condenastjohansens.com/warenhouse

NOTTINGHAMSHIRE - ARNOLD (NEAR NOTTINGHAM)

Cockliffe Country House Hotel

Burntstump Country Park, Burntstump Hill, Arnold, Nottinghamshire NG5 8PQ

Tel: 0115 968 0179
www.condenastjohansens.com/cockliffe

NOTTINGHAMSHIRE - NOTTINGHAM

Greenwood Lodge

5 Third Avenue, Sherwood Rise, Nottingham NG7 6JH

Tel: 0115 962 1206
www.condenastjohansens.com/greenwoodlodge

OXFORDSHIRE - BURFORD (COTSWOLDS)

Burford House

99 High Street, Burford, Oxfordshire OX18 4QA

Tel: 01993 823151
www.condenastjohansens.com/burfordhouse

OXFORDSHIRE - BURFORD (COTSWOLDS)

The Lamb Inn

Sheep Street, Burford, Oxfordshire OX18 4LR

Tel: 01993 823155
www.condenastjohansens.com/lambinnburford

OXFORDSHIRE - OXFORD (MINSTER LOVELL)

Old Swan & Minster Mill

Minster Lovell, Near Burford, Oxfordshire OX29 0RN

Tel: 01993 774441
www.condenastjohansens.com/milloldswan

Small Hotels, Inns & Restaurants - Great Britain & Ireland

Properties listed below can be found in our Recommended Small Hotels, Inns & Restaurants – Great Britain & Ireland 2013 Guide

OXFORDSHIRE - OXFORD (MURCOTT)

The Nut Tree Inn

Murcott, Kidlington, Oxfordshire OX5 2RE

Tel: 01865 331253
www.condenastjohansens.com/nuttreeinn

OXFORDSHIRE - WOODSTOCK

Hope House and Six Bells Apartment

Oxford Street, Woodstock, Oxfordshire OX20 1TS

Tel: 01993 815990
www.condenastjohansens.com/hopehouse

SHROPSHIRE - SHREWSBURY (WEM)

Soulton Hall

Near Wem, Shropshire SY4 5RS

Tel: 01939 232786
www.condenastjohansens.com/soultonhall

SOMERSET - MINEHEAD

Binham Grange

Old Cleeve, Near Minehead, Somerset TA24 6HX

Tel: 01984 640056
www.condenastjohansens.com/binhamgrange

SOMERSET - WELLS

Beryl

Wells, Somerset BA5 3JP

Tel: 01749 678738
www.condenastjohansens.com/beryl

STAFFORDSHIRE - MODDERSHALL (NEAR STONE)

Moddershall Oaks Country Spa Retreat

Moddershall, Stone, Staffordshire ST15 8TG

Tel: 01782 399000
www.condenastjohansens.com/moddershalloaks

SUFFOLK - MILDENHALL (NEAR NEWMARKET)

The Olde Bull Inn

The Street, Barton Mills, Bury St Edmunds, Suffolk IP28 6AA

Tel: 01638 711001
www.condenastjohansens.com/oldebullinn

SUFFOLK - SAXMUNDHAM (YOXFORD)

Satis House Hotel & Restaurant

Main Road, Yoxford, Saxmundham, Suffolk IP17 3EX

Tel: 01728 668418
www.condenastjohansens.com/satishouse

SURREY - CHIDDINGFOLD

The Swan Inn

Petworth Road, Chiddingfold, Surrey GU8 4TY

Tel: 01428 684688
www.condenastjohansens.com/swansurrey

WARWICKSHIRE - ROYAL LEAMINGTON SPA

Episode Hotel

64 Upper Holly Walk, Royal Leamington Spa, Warwickshire CV32 4JL

Tel: 01926 883777
www.condenastjohansens.com/epsiode

WARWICKSHIRE - SHIPSTON-ON-STOUR (NEAR STRATFORD-UPON-AVON)

The George Hotel

High Street, Shipston-on-Stour, Warwickshire CV36 4AJ

Tel: 01608 661453
www.condenastjohansens.com/georgeshipston

WILTSHIRE - CASTLE COMBE

The Castle Inn

Castle Combe, Wiltshire SN14 7HN

Tel: 01249 783030
www.condenastjohansens.com/castleinn

WORCESTERSHIRE - IPSLEY (NEAR REDDITCH)

The Old Rectory

Ipsley Lane, Ipsley, Near Redditch, Worcestershire B98 0AP

Tel: 01527 523000
www.condenastjohansens.com/oldrecipsley

WORCESTERSHIRE - UPTON-UPON-SEVERN (NEAR MALVERN)

The White Lion Hotel

High Street, Upton-upon-Severn, Near Malvern, Worcestershire WR8 0HJ

Tel: 01684 592551
www.condenastjohansens.com/whitelionupton

NORTH YORKSHIRE - AUSTWICK (YORKSHIRE DALES)

The Traddock

Austwick, North Yorkshire LA2 8BY

Tel: 015242 51224
www.condenastjohansens.com/austwick

MONAGHAN - GLASLOUGH

Castle Leslie Estate

Castle Leslie Estate, Glaslough, County Monaghan

Tel: 00 353 47 88100
www.condenastjohansens.com/castleleslie

Small Hotels, Inns & Restaurants - Great Britain & Ireland

Properties listed below can be found in our Recommended Small Hotels, Inns & Restaurants – Great Britain & Ireland 2013 Guide

ABERDEENSHIRE - BALLATER (ROYAL DEESIDE)

Darroch Learg

Braemar Road, Ballater, Aberdeenshire AB35 5UX

Tel: 013397 55443
www.condenastjohansens.com/darrochlearg

ANGUS - FORFAR

Kinnettles Castle

Forfar, Angus, DD8 1TR

Tel: 01494 682682
www.condenastjohansens.com/kinnettlescastle

ARGYLL & BUTE - OBAN

The Manor House Hotel

Gallanach Road, Oban, Argyll & Bute PA34 4LS

Tel: 01631 562087
www.condenastjohansens.com/manorhouseoban

ARGYLL & BUTE - STRONTIAN

Kilcamb Lodge Hotel & Restaurant

Strontian, Argyll & Bute PH36 4HY

Tel: 01967 402257
www.condenastjohansens.com/kilcamblodge

DUMFRIES & GALLOWAY - AUCHENCAIRN (CASTLE DOUGLAS)

Balcary Bay Hotel

Auchencairn, Castle Douglas, Dumfries & Galloway DG7 1QZ

Tel: 01556 640217
www.condenastjohansens.com/balcarybay

EAST LOTHIAN - MUSSELBURGH

Carberry Tower

Musselburgh, East Lothian EH21 8PY

Tel: 0131 665 3135
www.condenastjohansens.com/carberrytower

EDINBURGH

The Howard

34 Great King Street, Edinburgh EH3 6QH

Tel: 0131 5573500
www.condenastjohansens.com/thehoward

HIGHLAND - CAITHNESS

Ackergill Tower

By Wick, Caithness, KW1 4RG

Tel: 01955 603556
www.condenastjohansens.com/ackergilltower

HIGHLAND - INVERNESS

Loch Ness Lodge

Brachla, Loch Ness-side, Inverness IV3 8LA

Tel: 01456 459469
www.condenastjohansens.com/lochnesslodge

HIGHLAND - ISLE OF SKYE (SLEAT)

Toravaig House

Knock Bay, Sleat, Isle of Skye IV44 8RE

Tel: 01471 820200
www.condenastjohansens.com/toravaig

HIGHLAND - NAIRN

Inveran Lodge

Seafield Street, Nairn, Inverness-shire IV12 4HG

Tel: 01667 455 666
www.condenastjohansens.com/inveranlodge

HIGHLAND - SOUTH LOCH NESS (BY INVERNESS)

The Steadings at The Grouse & Trout

Flichity by Farr, South Loch Ness, Inverness IV2 6XD

Tel: 01808 521314
www.condenastjohansens.com/steadings

CEREDIGION - CARDIGAN (GLYNARTHEN)

Penbontbren

Glynarthen, Near Cardigan, Llandysul, Ceredigion SA44 6PE

Tel: 01239 810248
www.condenastjohansens.com/penbontbren

DENBIGHSHIRE - DENBIGH (NEAR RUTHIN)

Pentre Mawr Country House

Llandyrnog, Denbigh, North Wales LL16 4LA

Tel: 01824 790732
www.condenastjohansens.com/pentremawr

GWYNEDD - ABERSOCH

Porth Tocyn Country House Hotel

Abersoch, Pwllheli, Gwynedd LL53 7BU

Tel: 01758 713303
www.condenastjohansens.com/porthtocyn

GWYNEDD - BARMOUTH (LLANABER)

Llwyndu Farmhouse

Llanaber, Nr Barmouth, Gwynedd LL42 1RR

Tel: 01341 280144
www.condenastjohansens.com/llwyndu

Small Hotels, Inns & Restaurants - Great Britain & Ireland

Properties listed below can be found in our Recommended Small Hotels, Inns & Restaurants – Great Britain & Ireland 2012 Guide

ISLE OF ANGLESEY - BEAUMARIS

Plas Rhianfa

Beaumaris, Isle of Anglesey LL59 5NS

Tel: 01248 713656

www.condenastjohansens.com/plasrhianfa

MONMOUTHSHIRE - TREDUNNOCK (NEAR USK)

Newbridge On Usk

Tredunnock, Near Usk, Monmouthshire NP15 1LY

Tel: 01633 410262

www.condenastjohansens.com/newbridgeonusk

MONMOUTHSHIRE - MONMOUTH (SKENFRITH)

The Bell At Skenfrith

Skenfrith, Monmouthshire NP7 8UH

Tel: 01600 750235

www.condenastjohansens.com/bellskenfrith

Looking for the Perfect Gift...

Why not treat someone to our Gift Vouchers!

The perfect gift for birthdays, weddings and anniversaries for friends, family, special clients and colleagues.

Gift Vouchers are valid for one year and are redeemable against most hotel services within our portfolio of Recommended Hotels, Spas & Venues including accommodation and dining.

Vouchers are available in denominations of £100, £50, $150, $75 , €140, €70, and may be used as payment or part payment for your stay or a meal at any Condé Nast Johansens 2013 recommended property.

For more information visit www.condenastjohansens.com/gift-vouchers

Other Condé Nast Johansens Guides

To purchase Guides please call +44 (0) 208 995 7067
or visit our Bookshop at www.condenastjohansens.com/books

Like you, we're **recommended** by Condé Nast Johansens

As the preferred insurance partner of Condé Nast Johansens, JLT Specialty is best placed to make a **first class difference** to your insurance needs.

JLT Specialty has a specialist team with over 20 years experience in the global hotel industry. Our clients include some of the worlds most luxurious hotels.

The difference comes from our understanding of the way we present your risks to the insurance market and work with underwriters to maximise the best terms for you. Through our enthusiasm, attention to detail and commitment, we can build you a tailor-made solution set around your individual requirements at a competitive price.

To learn more about JLT Specialty contact

Sharon Murphy
Tel: +44 (0)20 7528 4247
Email: sharon_murphy@jltgroup.com

Margaret Booroff
Tel: +44 (0)20 7558 3701
Email: margaret_booroff@jltgroup.com

INSURANCE BROKING • INNOVATION
RISK IDENTIFICATION AND MANAGEMENT • DISASTER RECOVERY

JLT Specialty Limited. Lloyd's Broker. Authorised and Regulated by the Financial Services Authority. A member of the Jardine Lloyd Thompson Group. Registered Office: 6 Crutched Friars, London EC3N 2PH. Registered in England No. 01536540. VAT No. 244 2321 96.
265601

JLT

Historic Houses, Castles & Gardens

We are pleased to feature over 150 places to visit during your stay at a Condé Nast Johansens Recommendation.
More information about these attractions, including opening times and entry fees, can be found on www.historichouses.co.uk

England

Bedfordshire

John Bunyan Museum & Library – Bunyan Meeting Free Church, Mill Street, Bedford, Bedfordshire MK40 3EU. Tel: 01234 213722
Queen Anne's Summerhouse – Shuttleworth Estate, Old Warden, Bedfordshire SG18 9EP. Tel: 01628 825925
Moggerhanger Park – Park Road, Moggerhanger, Bedfordshire MK44 3RW. Tel: 01767 641007

Berkshire

Eton College – The Visits Office, Eton High Street, Windsor, Berkshire SL4 6DW. Tel: 01753 671177
Welford Park – Newbury, Berkshire RG20 8HU. Tel: 01488 608203 / 608691

Buckinghamshire

Nether Winchendon House – Nr Aylesbury, Buckinghamshire HP18 0DY. Tel: 01844 290101
Waddesdon Manor – Waddesdon, Nr Aylesbury, Buckinghamshire HP18 0JH. Tel: 01296 653226

Cambridgeshire

Island Hall – Post Street, Godmanchester, Cambridgeshire PE29 2BA. Tel: 01480 459676
The Manor – Hemingford Grey, Huntingdon, Cambridgeshire PE28 9BN. Tel: 01480 463134

Cheshire

Dorfold Hall – Nantwich, Cheshire CW5 8LD. Tel: 01270 625245
Peover Hall – Peover Estate, Over Peover, Knutsford, Cheshire WA16 9HW. Tel: 01565 724 220

Rode Hall – Scholar Green (by Stoke-on-Trent), Cheshire ST7 3QP. Tel: 01270 882961 / 873237
Tabley House Collection – Knutsford, Cheshire WA16 0HB. Tel: 01565 750 151

Cornwall

Caerhays Castle and Estate – Estate Office, Gorran, St. Austell, Cornwall PL26 6LY. Tel: 01872 501310 / 501144
Mount Edgcumbe House & Country Park – Cremyll, Torpoint, Cornwall PL10 1HZ. Tel: 01752 822236
Pencarrow House and Gardens – Washway, Bodmin, Cornwall PL30 3AG. Tel: 01208 841369
Prideaux Place – Padstow, Cornwall PL28 8RP. Tel: 01841 532411

Cumbria

The Beatrix Potter Gallery – Main Street, Hawkshead, Cumbria LA22 ONS. Tel: 015394 36355

Dove Cottage & The Wordsworth Museum – The Wordsworth Trust, Dove Cottage, Grasmere, Cumbria LA22 9SH. Tel: 015394 35544
Isel Hall – Cockermouth, Cumbria CA13 OQG. Tel: 01900 826127

Derbyshire

Haddon Hall – Bakewell, Derbyshire DE45 1LA. Tel: 01629 812855
Melbourne Hall & Gardens – Melbourne, Derbyshire DE73 8EN. Tel: 01332 862502
Renishaw Hall and Gardens – Nr Sheffield, Derbyshire S21 3WB. Tel: 01246 432210

Devon

Bowringsleigh – Kingsbridge, Devon TQ7 3LL. Tel: 01548 852014
Downes – Crediton, Devon EX17 3PL. Tel: 01363 775142
Powderham Castle – Kenton, Exeter, Devon EX6 8JQ. Tel: 01626 890243
Torre Abbey – The Kings Drive, Torquay, Devon TQ2 5JX. Tel: 01803 293593

Dorset

Chiffchaffs – Chaffeymoor, Bourton, Gillingham, Dorset SP8 5BY. Tel: 01747 840841
Clavell Tower – Kimmeridge, Nr Wareham, Dorset. Tel: 01628 825925
Moignes Court – Owermoigne, Dorchester, Dorset DT2 8HY. Tel: 01305 853300
Russell-Cotes Art Gallery & Museum – Russell-Cotes Road, East Cliff, Bournemouth, Dorset BH1 3AA. Tel: 01202 451858

Essex

Ingatestone Hall – Hall Lane, Ingatestone, Essex CM4 9NR. Tel: 01277 353010

Gloucestershire

Berkeley Castle – Berkeley, Gloucestershire GL13 9BQ. Tel: 01453 810332
Bourton House Garden – Bourton-on-the-Hill, Near Moreton-in-Marsh, Gloucestershire GL56 9AE. Tel: 01386 700754
Cheltenham Art Gallery & Museum – Clarence Street, Cheltenham, Gloucestershire GL50 3JT. Tel: 01242 237431
Hardwicke Court – Nr Gloucester, Gloucestershire GL2 4RS. Tel: 01452 720212
Nature In Art - Wallsworth Hall – Wallsworth Hall, Main A38, Twigworth, Gloucestershire GL2 9PA. Tel: 01452 731422
Sezincote House & Garden – Near Moreton-in-Marsh, Gloucestershire GL56 9AW. Tel: 01386 700444
Sudeley Castle – Winchcombe, Gloucestershire GL54 5JD. Tel: 01242 602308

Historic Houses, Castles & Gardens

We are pleased to feature over 150 places to visit during your stay at a Condé Nast Johansens Recommendation.
More information about these attractions, including opening times and entry fees, can be found on www.historichouses.co.uk

Hampshire

Avington Park – Winchester, Hampshire SO21 1DB. Tel: 01962 779260
Greywell Hill House – Greywell, Hook, Hampshire RG29 1DG. Tel: 01256 703565
Houghton Lodge Gardens and Hampshire Hydroponicum – Houghton, Stockbridge, Hampshire SO20 6LQ. Tel: 01264 810912 / 810502

Hertfordshire

Gorhambury – St Albans, Hertfordshire AL3 6AH. Tel: 01727 854051

Isle of Wight

Deacons Nursery (H.H) – Moor View, Godshill, Isle of Wight PO38 3HW. Tel: 01983 840750 / 522243
Nunwell House and Gardens – West Lane, Brading, Isle of Wight PO36 OJQ. Tel: 01983 407240

Kent

Belmont House and Gardens – Belmont Park, Throwley, Faversham, Kent ME13 0HH. Tel: 01795 890202
Cobham Hall – Cobham, Nr Gravesend, Kent DA12 3BL. Tel: 01474 823371
The Grange – Ramsgate, Kent CT11 9NY. Tel: 01628 825925
Hever Castle and Gardens – Nr Edenbridge, Kent TN8 7NG. Tel: 01732 861710
Hole Park Garden – Hole Park, Rolvenden, Cranbrook, Kent TN17 4JA. Tel: 01580 241344
Mount Ephraim Gardens – Staple Street, Hernhill, Nr Faversham, Kent ME13 9TX. Tel: 01227 751496
The New College of Cobham – Cobhambury Road, Cobham, Nr Gravesend, Kent DA12 3BG. Tel: 01474 812503
Riverhill Himalayan Gardens – Riverhill, Sevenoaks, Kent TN15 ORR. Tel: 01732 459777

Leicestershire

Stapleford Park – Stappleford Park, Nr Melton Mowbray, Leicestershire LE14 2EF. Tel: 01572 787000

London

Burgh House & Hampstead Museum – New End Square, Hampstead, London NW3 1LT. Tel: 020 7431 0144
Chelsea Physic Garden – 66 Royal Hospital Road, Chelsea, London SW3 4HS. Tel: 020 7352 5646
Handel House Museum – 25 Brook Street, London W1K 4HB. Tel: 020 7495 1685
Pitzhanger Manor House – Walpole Park, Mattock Lane, Ealing, London W5 5EQ. Tel: 020 8567 1227
Spencer House – 27 St. James's Place, London SW1A 1NR. Tel: 020 7514 1958
Strawberry Hill House – 268 Waldegrave Road, Twickenham, London TW1 4ST. Tel: 020 8744 1241
Syon Park – Syon Park, Brentford, London TW8 8JF. Tel: 020 8560 0882

Merseyside

Meols Hall – Churchtown, Southport, Merseyside PR9 7LZ. Tel: 01704 228326

Norfolk

South Elmham Hall – Hall Lane, St Cross, Harleston, Norfolk IP20 OPY. Tel: 01986 782526
Walsingham Abbey Grounds and Shirehall Museum – Common Place, Little Walsingham, Norfolk NR22 6BP. Tel: 01328 820510

Northamptonshire

Boughton House and Gardens – Boughton House, Kettering, Northamptonshire NN14 1BJ. Tel: 01536 515731
Sulgrave Manor – Manor Road, Sulgrave, Banbury, Northamptonshire OX17 2SD. Tel: 01295 760205

Northumberland

Alnwick Castle – Alnwick, Northumberland NE66 1NQ. Tel: 01665 510777
Bamburgh Castle – Bamburgh, Northumberland ME69 7DF. Tel: 01668 214208 / 214515
Chipchase Castle & Gardens – Wark on Tyne, Hexham, Northumberland NE48 3NT. Tel: 01434 230203

Oxfordshire

Blenheim Palace – Woodstock, Oxfordshire OX20 1PX. Tel: 0800 849 6500 (24 hour recorded message)
Kingston Bagpuize House – Abingdon, Oxfordshire OX13 5AX. Tel: 01865 820259
Mapledurham House & Watermill – Nr Reading, Oxfordshire RG4 7TR. Tel: 01189 723350
Stonor Park – Nr Henley-on-Thames, Oxfordshire RG9 6HF. Tel: 01491 638587

Wallingford Castle Gardens – Castle Street, Wallingford, Oxfordshire OX10 8DL. Tel: 01491 835373

Shropshire

Hodnet Hall Gardens – Hodnet, Market Drayton, Shropshire TF9 3NN. Tel: 01630 685786
Ludlow Castle – Castle Square, Ludlow, Shropshire SY8 1AY. Tel: 01584 874465
The White House – Aston Munslow, Shropshire. Tel: 01628 825925

Historic Houses, Castles & Gardens

We are pleased to feature over 150 places to visit during your stay at a Condé Nast Johansens Recommendation.
More information about these attractions, including opening times and entry fees, can be found on www.historichouses.co.uk

Somerset

Glastonbury Abbey – Abbey Gatehouse, Magdalene Street, Glastonbury, Somerset BA6 9EL. Tel: 01458 832267
Great House Farm – Wells Road, Theale, Wedmore, Somerset BS28 4SJ. Tel: 01934 713133
Kentsford – Washford, Watchet, Somerset TA23 0JD. Tel: 01984 631307
Orchard Wyndham – Williton, Taunton, Somerset TA4 4HH. Tel: 01984 632309
Robin Hood's Hut – Halswell, Goathurst, Somerset. Tel: 01628 825925
Woodlands Castle – Woodlands, Ruishton, Taunton, Somerset TA3 5LU. Tel: 01823 444955

Staffordshire

Whitmore Hall – Whitmore, Newcastle-under-Lyme, Staffordshire ST5 5HW. Tel: 01782 680478

Suffolk

Freston Tower – Near Ipswich, Suffolk IP9 1AD. Tel: 01628 825925

Kentwell Hall – Long Melford, Sudbury, Suffolk CO10 9BA. Tel: 01787 310207

Surrey

Goddards – Abinger Common, Dorking, Surrey. Tel: 01628 825920
Loseley Park – Guildford, Surrey GU3 1HS. Tel: 01483 304440
Painshill Park Landscape Garden – Portsmouth Road, Cobham, Surrey KT11 1JE. Tel: 01932 868113
Titsey Place and Gardens – Titsey, Oxted, Surrey RH8 0SD. Tel: 01273 715356

East Sussex

Bentley Wildfowl & Motor Museum – Halland, Nr Lewes, East Sussex BN8 5AF. Tel: 01825 840573
Firle Place – Nr Lewes, East Sussex BN8 6LP. Tel: 01273 858307
Great Dixter House, Gardens & Nurseries – Great Dixter, Northiam, Rye, East Sussex TN31 6PH. Tel: 01797 252878
Merriments Gardens – Hawkhurst Road, Hurst Green, East Sussex TN19 7RA. Tel: 01580 860666
Pashley Manor Gardens – Ticehurst, East Sussex TN5 7HE. Tel: 01580 200888
Wilmington Priory – Wilmington, Nr Eastbourne, East Sussex BN26 5SW. Tel: 01628 825925

West Sussex

Arundel Castle – Arundel, West Sussex BN18 9AB. Tel: 01903 882173
Borde Hill – Borde Hill Lane, Haywards Heath, West Sussex RH16 1XP. Tel: 01444 450326
Cowdray – Visitor Centre, River Ground Stables, Midhurst, West Sussex GU29 9AL. Tel: 01730 810781
Goodwood House – Goodwood, Chichester, West Sussex PO18 0PX. Tel: 01243 755048
High Beeches Gardens – Handcross, West Sussex RH17 6HQ. Tel: 01444 400589
Parham House & Gardens – Parham Park, Storrington, Nr Pulborough, West Sussex RH20 4HS. Tel: 01903 742021

Warwickshire

Arbury Hall – Nuneaton, Warwickshire CV10 7PT. Tel: 02476 382804
Astley Castle – Astley, Nr Nuneaton, Warwickshire CV10 7QD. Tel: 01628 512128
Baddesley Clinton Hall – Rising Lane, Baddesley Clinton Village, Knowle, Solihull, Warwickshire B93 0DQ. Tel: 01564 783294
Compton Verney – Compton Verney, Warwickshire CV35 9HZ. Tel: 01926 645500
Coughton Court – Alcester, Warwickshire B49 5JA. Tel: 01789 400777
Packwood House – Packwood Lane, Lapworth, Warwickshire B94 6AT. Tel: 01564 782024

Stoneleigh Abbey – Kenilworth, Warwickshire CV8 2LF. Tel: 01926 858585

West Midlands

The Barber Institute of Fine Arts – University of Birmingham, Edgbaston, Birmingham, West Midlands B15 2TS. Tel: 0121 414 7333
The Birmingham Botanical Gardens & Glasshouses – Westbourne Road, Edgbaston, Birmingham, West Midlands B15 3TR. Tel: 0121 454 1860

Wiltshire

Iford Manor: The Peto Gardens – Bradford-on-Avon, Wiltshire BA15 2BA. Tel: 01225 863 146
Longleat – Estate Office, Warminster, Wiltshire, Wiltshire BA12 7NW. Tel: 01985 844328

Worcestershire

Harvington Hall – Harvington, Kidderminster, Worcestershire DY10 4LR. Tel: 01562 777846
Spetchley Park Gardens – Spetchley Park, Worcestershire WR5 1RS. Tel: 01453 810303

East Yorkshire

Burton Agnes Hall & Gardens – Burton Agnes, Diffield, East Yorkshire YO25 4NB. Tel: 01262 490324

North Yorkshire

Allerton Castle – Allerton Castle, Allerton Mauleverer, Knaresborough, North Yorkshire HG5 0SE. Tel: 01423 330 927
Brockfield Hall – Warthill, York, North Yorkshire YO19 5XJ. Tel: 01904 489 362
Constable Burton Hall – Leyburn, North Yorkshire DL8 5LJ. Tel: 01677 450428
The Forbidden Corner – Tupgill Park Estate, Coverham, Nr Middleham, North Yorkshire DL8 4TJ. Tel: 01969 640638
Fountains Abbey and Studley Royal Water Garden – Ripon, Nr Harrogate, North Yorkshire HG4 3DY. Tel: 01765 608888
Kiplin Hall – Nr Scorton, Richmond, North Yorkshire DL10 6AT. Tel: 01748 818178
Newby Hall and Gardens – Ripon, North Yorkshire HG4 5AE. Information Hotline: 0845 4504068 Estate Office: 01423 322583
Skipton Castle – Skipton, North Yorkshire BD23 1AW. Tel: 01756 792442

Historic Houses, Castles & Gardens

We are pleased to feature over 150 places to visit during your stay at a Condé Nast Johansens Recommendation.
More information about these attractions, including opening times and entry fees, can be found on www.historichouses.co.uk

West Yorkshire

Ledston Hall – Hall Lane, Ledston, Castleford, West Yorkshire WF10 2BB. Tel: 01423 523 423
Nostell Priory – Wakefield, West Yorkshire WF4 1QE. Tel: 01924 863892

Northern Ireland

Co Down

Mount Stewart House and Gardens – Portaferry Road, Newtownards, Co Down BT22 2AD. Tel: 028 4278 8387/ 7817

Co Londonderry

Downhill Demesne and Hezlett House – 107 Sea Road, Castlerock, Coleraine, Co Londonderry BT51 4TW. Tel: 028 7084 8728

Ireland

Cork

Blarney Castle, House and Garden – Blarney, Cork. Tel: 00 353 21 4385252

Kildare

The Irish National Stud & Gardens – The Irish National Stud, Tully, Kildare Town, Kildare. Tel: 00 353 45 521617

Westmeath

Tullynally Castle Gardens – Tullynally Estate, Castlepollard, Westmeath. Tel: 00 353 44 966 1159

Scotland

Aberdeenshire

Arbuthnott House – Arbuthnott, Laurencekirk, Aberdeenshire AB30 1PA. Tel: 01561 320417
Provost Skene's House – Guestrow (off Broad Street), Aberdeen, Aberdeenshire AB10 1AS. Tel: 01224 641086

Ayrshire

Kelburn Castle and Country Centre – Kelburn, Fairlie (Nr Largs), Ayrshire KA29 0BE. Tel: 01475 568685

North Ayrshire

Auchinleck House – Ochiltree, North Ayrshire. Tel: 01628 825925

Dumfries & Galloway

Ardwell Gardens – Ardwell House, Ardwell, Stranraer, Dumfries & Galloway DG9 9LY. Tel: 01776 860227
Castle Kennedy Gardens – The Estates Office, Rephad, Stranraer, Dumfries & Galloway DG9 8BX. Tel: 01776 702 024
Drumlanrig Castle, Gardens & Country Park – Thornhill, Dumfriesshire, Dumfries & Galloway DG3 4AQ. Tel: 01848 331555
Glenmalloch Lodge – Newton Stewart, Dumfries & Galloway. Tel: 01628 825925

Fife

Cambo Gardens – Cambo Estate, Kingbarns, St. Andrews, Fife KY16 8QD. Tel: 01333 450054
Scotland's Secret Bunker – Crown Buildings, Troywood, Nr St Andrews, Fife KY16 8QH. Tel: 01333 310301

Highland

Dunvegan Castle & Gardens – The MacLeod Estate Office, Dunvegan, Isle of Skye, Highland IV55 8WF. Tel: 01470 521206
Mount Stuart – Mount Stuart, Isle of Bute, Highland PA20 9LR. Tel: 01700 503877
Scone Palace – Scone, Perth, Perthshire, Highland PH2 6BD. Tel: 01738 552300

East Lothian

Lennoxlove House – Lennoxlove Estate, Haddington, East Lothian EH41 4NZ. Tel: 01620 828608

West Lothian

Newliston – Kirkliston, West Lothian EH29 9EB. Tel: 0131 333 3231

Scottish Borders

Abbotsford The Home of Sir Walter Scott – Melrose, Scottish Borders TD6 9BQ. Tel: 01896 752 043
Bowhill House & Country Park – Bowhill, Selkirk, Scottish Borders TD7 5ET. Tel: 01750 22204
Floors Castle – Kelso, Scottish Borders TD5 7SF. Tel: 01573 223333
Manderston – Duns, Berwickshire, Scottish Borders TD11 3PP. Tel: 01361 883 450

Mellerstain House and Gardens – The Mellerstain Trust, Gordon, Berwickshire, Scottish Borders TD3 6LG. Tel: 01573 410225
Paxton House, Gallery & Country Park – Paxton, Nr Berwick upon Tweed, Scottish Borders TD15 1SZ. Tel: 01289 386291
Traquair House – Innerleithen, Peebles, Scottish Borders EH44 6PW. Tel: 01896 830 323

Wales

Denbighshire

Dolbelydr – Trefnant, Denbighshire. Tel: 01628 825925

Monmouthshire

Usk Castle – Castle House, Monmouth Rd, Usk, Monmouthshire NP15 1SD. Tel: 01291 672563

Pembrokeshire

St David's Cathedral – The Deanery, The Close, St Davids, Pembrokeshire SA62 6RH. Tel: 01437 720 202

Powys

The Judge's Lodging – Broad Street, Presteigne, Mid Wales, Powys LD8 2AD. Tel: 01544 260650

France

Loire Valley

Château de Chenonceau – 37150 Chenonceaux, Loire Valley 37150. Tel: 00 33 2 47 23 44 06

Martinvast

Chateau et Parc de Martinvast – Domaine de Beaurepaire, 50690 Martinvast, Basse-Normandie, France 50690. Tel: 00 33 2 33 87 20 80

Gold Key Media

Gold Key Media is the World's largest supplier of magazines to the hotel and leisure industry. We have a range of over 200 international magazine titles to choose from at the most competitive prices available. We help you to ensure your guests relax in the comfort of your hotel and spa.

Gold Key Media is proud to supply the most desirable and recognised hotels and venues in the world.
We work with the most established and recognised titles in the publishing industry to provide you with the best discounts on Newspaper and Magazine volumes for your business.
All our clients are given a dedicated and personalised service.
www.goldkeymedia.co.uk or call +44 (0) 20 7491 4065

Wait and read provide quality magazine subscription packs for businesses at exceptional discounts.
Save up to 80% off the cover price.
No Minimum Orders.
Courier Deliveries
Direct Debit Option.
Create your bespoke pack from over 100 monthly and weekly titles.
www.waitandread.co.uk or call +44 (0) 18 9543 3733

MAGAZINE **CAFÉ**

Offering single issue, single copy to full-year subscriptions of your favourite magazines, you need never miss an issue again.
Magazine Café offers UK and international magazines in all categories to suit all tastes, whether for yourself or as a gift. Whatever you are interested in reading about, Magazine Café has it covered.
To see the extensive selection of international titles and details of how to order, please go to our website.
www.magazinecafe.co.uk or call +44 (0) 18 9543 3722

Hotels, Europe & The Mediterranean

All the properties listed below can be found in our Recommended Hotels & Spas, Europe & The Mediterranean 2013 Guide.

Austria

Hotel the Crystal .... Tirol .... +43 5 256 6454

Belgium

Hotel de Orangerie .... Bruges .... +32 50 341649
Manoir du Dragon .... Knokke~Heist .... +32 50 63 05 80
Hostellerie Ter Driezen .... Turnhout .... +32 14 41 87 57

Channel Islands

The Atlantic Hotel .... Jersey .... +44 1534 744101

Croatia

Kazbek .... Dubrovnik .... +385 20 362 900
Villa Anastasia .... Dubrovnik .... +385 91 5347 734
Villa Dubrovnik .... Dubrovnik .... +385 20 500 300
Villa Tuttorotto .... Rovinj .... +385 52 815 181
Hotel Heritage Martinis Marchi .... Solta Island .... +385 21 572 768

Egypt

Farah Nile Cruise .... Luxor - Aswan .... +202 2418 5456/86

France

Hostellerie Les Bas Rupts Le Chalet Fleuri ....
Alsace~Lorraine .... +33 3 29 63 09 25
Hôtel à la Cour d'Alsace .... Alsace~Lorraine .... +33 3 88 95 07 00
Hôtel Les Têtes .... Alsace~Lorraine .... +33 3 89 24 43 43
Romantik Hôtel le Maréchal .... Alsace~Lorraine .... +33 3 89 41 60 32
Domaine de Rochevilaine .... Brittany .... +33 2 97 41 61 61
Ti al Lannec & Spa .... Brittany .... +33 2 96 15 01 01
Abbaye de la Bussière .... Burgundy .... +33 3 80 49 02 29
Château Hôtel André Ziltener .... Burgundy .... +33 3 80 62 41 62
La Borde .... Burgundy .... +33 3 86 47 69 01
Château d'Etoges .... Champagne~Ardenne .... +33 3 26 59 30 08
Domaine de Barive .... Champagne~Ardenne .... +33 3 23 22 15 15
Hôtel Le Pinarello .... Corsica .... +33 4 95 71 44 39
Château Eza .... Côte d'Azur .... +33 4 93 41 12 24
Hôtel Le Bailli de Suffren .... Côte d'Azur .... +33 4 75 75 21 91
La Villa Mauresque .... Côte d'Azur .... +33 494 83 02 42
Le Mas Candille .... Côte d'Azur .... +33 4 92 28 43 43
Château de l'Abbaye .... Loire Valley .... +33 251 56 17 56
Château de Pray .... Loire Valley .... +33 247 57 23 67
Le Manoir Saint Thomas .... Loire Valley .... +33 2 47 23 21 82
Château la Chenevière .... Normandy .... +33 2 31 51 25 25
Hôtel Duc de Saint~Simon .... Paris .... +33 1 44 39 20 20
Hotel La Belle Juliette .... Paris .... +33 1 42 22 97 40
Hotel Lancaster .... Paris .... +33 1 40 76 40 76
Hôtel San Régis .... Paris .... +33 1 44 95 16 16
Chalet Cragganmore .... Rhône~Alpes .... +44 131 558 1671
Chalet Hôtel Kaya .... Rhône~Alpes .... +33 4 75 75 21 91
Chalet Hôtel La Marmotte, Ski, Golf & Spa ....
Rhône~Alpes .... +33 4 50 75 80 33
Le Fer à Cheval .... Rhône~Alpes .... +33 4 50 21 30 39

Château de Mirambeau .... South West .... +33 5 46 04 91 20
Le Boutique Hotel Bordeaux .... South West .... +33 5 56 48 80 40

Great Britain

The Arch London .... England .... +44 20 7724 4700
Beaufort House .... England .... +44 20 7584 2600
The French Horn .... England .... +44 1189 692 204
The May Fair .... England .... +44 20 7769 4041
The Mayflower Hotel .... England .... +44 20 7370 0991
The New Linden Hotel .... England .... +44 20 7221 4321
Sopwell House .... England .... +44 1727 864477
Twenty Nevern Square .... England .... +44 20 7565 9555

Hotels, Europe & The Mediterranean

All the properties listed below can be found in our Recommended Hotels & Spas, Europe & The Mediterranean 2013 Guide.

Greece

Domes of Elounda Boutique Beach Resort	Crete	+30 2310 810624
Knossos Beach Bungalows & Suites	Crete	+30 2810 761000
Pleiades Luxurious Villas	Crete	+30 2310 810624
Apanema Aegean Luxury Hotel & Suites Mykonos	Mykonos	+30 22890 28590
Archipelagos	Mykonos	+30 228 907 2012
Tharroe of Mykonos	Mykonos	+30 22890 27370
Andronis Boutique Hotel	Santorini	+30 22860 72182/4
Andronis Luxury Suites	Santorini	+30 22860 72041/2/3
Apanema Aegean Luxury Hotel & Suites	Santorini	+30 22860 85270/71/72
Astra Suites	Santorini	+30 22860 23641

Homeric Poems	**Santorini**	**+30 22860 24661**
Hotel Majestic	Santorini	+30 22860 25972
Mill Houses	Santorini	+30 22860 27117
Timedrops Santorini	Santorini	+30 2 28 60 83 282
White Santorini	Santorini	+30 22860 25257
Lesante Hotel & Spa	Zakynthos	+30 2 69 50 41 330

Italy

Casa Angelina Lifestyle	Campania	+39 089 8131333
Hotel Botanico San Lazzaro	Campania	+39 089 877750
Mezzatorre Resort & Spa	Campania	+39 081 986111
Terme Manzi Hotel & Spa	Campania	+39 081 99 47 22
Hotel Posta (Historical Residence)	Emilia Romagna	+39 05 22 43 29 44
Palazzo Dalla Rosa Prati	Emilia Romagna	+39 0521 386 429
Buonanotte Garibaldi	Lazio	+39 06 58 330 733
Casa Montani - Luxury Town House	Lazio	+39 06 3260 0421
Hotel dei Borgognoni	Lazio	+39 06 6994 1505
La Posta Vecchia	Lazio	+39 06 9949500
Parco dei Principi Grand Hotel & Spa	Lazio	+39 06 854421
Villa Spalletti Trivelli	Lazio	+39 06 48907934
Abbadia San Giorgio - Historical Residence	Liguria	+39 0185 491119
Cà de Tobia Luxury Guest House	Liguria	
Grand Hotel Bristol Resort & Spa	Liguria	+ 39 0185 273 313
Grand Hotel Diana Majestic	Liguria	+39 0183 402 727

Grand Hotel Miramare	**Liguria**	**+39 0185 287013**
Hotel Punta Est	Liguria	+39 019 600611
Hotel Vis à Vis	Liguria	+39 0185 42661
Camperio House Suites and Apartments	Lombardy	+39 02 303 22800
Hotel Bellerive	Lombardy	+39 0365 520 410
Hotel de la Ville & La Villa	Lombardy	+39 039 39421
Hotel Manzoni	Lombardy	+39 027 600 5700
L'Albereta	Lombardy	+39 030 7760 550
Albergo L'Ostelliere	Piemonte	+39 0143 607 801
Relais Bella Rosina	Piemonte	+39 011 9233600
Relais San Maurizio	Piemonte	+39 0141 841900
Hotel Lucrezia	Sardinia	+39 0783 412078
Hotel Relais Villa del Golfo & Spa	Sardinia	+ 39 0789 892091
Petra Segreta Resort & SPA	Sardinia	+39 0789 187 6441
Su Gologone - Country Art Resort	Sardinia	+39 0784 287512
Baia Taormina Grand Palace Hotels & Spa	Sicily	+39 0942 756292
Donna Carmela Resort	Sicily	+39 095 809383
Hotel Signum	Sicily	+39 090 9844222
Locanda Don Serafino	Sicily	+39 0932 220065
Palazzo Failla Hotel	Sicily	+39 0932 941059
Castel Fragsburg	Trentino - Alto Adige / Dolomites	+39 0473 244071
Du Lac et Du Parc Grand Resort	Trentino - Alto Adige / Dolomites	+39 0464 566600
feldmilla. designhotel	Trentino - Alto Adige / Dolomites	+39 0474 677100
Hotel Ciasa Salares	Trentino - Alto Adige / Dolomites	+39 0471 849445
Hotel Gardena Grödnerhof	Trentino - Alto Adige / Dolomites	+39 0471 796315

Hotels, Europe & The Mediterranean

All the properties listed below can be found in our Recommended Hotels & Spas, Europe & The Mediterranean 2013 Guide.

Lido Palace .... Trentino - Alto Adige / Dolomites.+39 0464 021899

Meisters Hotel Irma - Villa Amore .... Trentino - Alto Adige / Dolomites+39 0473 212 000

Miramonti Boutique Hotel .... Trentino - Alto Adige / Dolomites+39 0473 27 9335

Parkhotel Holzner .... Trentino - Alto Adige / Dolomites+39 0471 345 231

Albergo Pietrasanta - Palazzo Barsanti Bonetti .... Tuscany .... +39 0584 793 727

Albergo Villa Casanova .... Tuscany .... +39 0583 369000

Borgo Scopeto Relais .... Tuscany .... +39 0577 320001

Castello del Nero Hotel & Spa .... Tuscany .... +39 055 806 470

Country House Casa Cornacchi .... Tuscany .... +39 055 998229

Country Relais Villa L'Olmo .... Tuscany .... +39 055 23 11 311

Golden Tower Hotel & Spa .... Tuscany .... +39 055 287 860

Granduomo Charming Accommodation .... Tuscany .... +39 055 267 0004

Hotel Brunelleschi .... Tuscany .... +39 055 27370

Hotel Byron .... Tuscany .... +39 0584 787 052

Hotel Plaza e de Russie .... Tuscany .... +39 0584 44449

Hotel Tornabuoni Beacci .... Tuscany .... +39 055 212645

Il Bottaccio .... Tuscany .... +39 0585 340031

Il Pellicano Hotel .... Tuscany .... +39 0564 858111

L'Andana .... Tuscany .... +39 0564 944 800

Lucignanello Bandini (Borgo Storico) .... Tuscany .... +39 0577 803 068

Marignolle Relais & Charme .... Tuscany .... +39 055 228 6910

Monsignor Della Casa Country Resort & Spa .... Tuscany .... +39 055 840 821

Palazzo Magnani Feroni - all-suites florence .... Tuscany .... +39 055 2399544

Relais Badia di Campoleone .... Tuscany .... +39 0575 451588

Relais la Suvera (Dimora Storica) .... Tuscany .... +39 0577 960 300

Relais Osteria dell'Orcia .... Tuscany .... + 39 0577 887111

Relais Villa Belpoggio (Historical House) .... Tuscany .... +39 055 9694411

Tenuta San Pietro Luxury Hotel & Restaurant .... Tuscany .... +39 0583 926676

Tombolo Talasso Resort .... Tuscany .... +39 0565 74530

Villa Armena Luxury Relais .... Tuscany .... +39 057 780 8433

Villa Campestri Olive Oil Resort .... Tuscany .... +39 055 849 0107

Villa Curina Resort .... Tuscany .... +39 0577 355630

Villa le Barone .... Tuscany .... +39 055 852621

Castello di Petroia .... Umbria .... +39 075 92 02 87

Tenuta di Canonica .... Umbria .... +39 075 8947545

Romantik Hotel Jolanda Sport .... Valle d'Aosta .... +39 0125 366 140

Albergo Quattro Fontane - Residenza d'Epoca .... Veneto .... +39 041 526 0227

Ca Maria Adele .... Veneto .... +39 041 52 03 078

Ca' Sagredo Hotel .... Veneto .... +39 041 2413111

Color Hotel style & design .... Veneto .... +39 045 621 0857

Hotel Caesius Thermae & SPA Resort .... Veneto .... +39 045 7219100

Londra Palace .... Veneto .... +39 041 5200533

Palazzo Selvadego .... Veneto .... + 39 041 5200211

Villa Cordevigo .... Veneto .... +39 045 723 5287

Villa d'Acquarone .... Veneto .... +39 342 782 8341

Montenegro

Palazzo Radomiri .... Kotor .... +382 32 333 172

Morocco

Palais Shéhérazade & Spa .... Fes .... +212 535 741 642

Kasbah Du Toubkal .... High Atlas Mountains .... +212 524 48 56 11

The Netherlands

Ambassade Hotel .... Amsterdam .... +31 20 5550 222

Hotels, Europe & The Mediterranean

All the properties listed below can be found in our Recommended Hotels & Spas, Europe & The Mediterranean 2013 Guide.

Portugal

Convento do Espinheiro, A Luxury Collection Hotel & Spa .... Alentejo .... +351 266 788 200

L'AND Vineyards Resort .... Alentejo .... +351 266 242 400

Pine Cliffs Terraces and Villas .... Algarve .... +351 289 500 100

Tivoli Marina Vilamoura .... Algarve .... +351 218 507 708

Tivoli Victoria .... Algarve .... +351 218 507 708

Altis Belém Hotel & Spa .... Lisbon & Tagus Valley .... +351 210 400 200

As Janelas Verdes .... Lisbon & Tagus Valley .... +351 21 39 68 143

Chiado16-Premium Accommodation .... Lisbon & Tagus Valley .... +351 394 1616

Heritage Av Liberdade .... Lisbon & Tagus Valley .... +351 213 404 040

Hotel Albatroz .... Lisbon & Tagus Valley .... +351 21 484 73 80

Hotel Britania .... Lisbon & Tagus Valley .... +351 21 31 55 016

Lisboa Plaza Hotel .... Lisbon & Tagus Valley .... +351 213 218 218

Palácio Estoril, Hotel, Golf & Spa .... Lisbon & Tagus Valley .... +351 21 464 80 00

Sofitel Lisbon Liberdade .... Lisbon & Tagus Valley .... +351 21 322 83 00

Solar do Castelo .... Lisbon & Tagus Valley .... +351 218 806 050

Vidago Palace .... Oporto & Northern Portugal .... +351 276 990 920

The Yeatman Hotel .... Oporto & Northern Portugal .... +351 22 013 3100

Slovenia

Antiq Palace Hotel & Spa d.o.o. .... Ljubljana .... +386 838 96 700

Spain

Barceló la Bobadilla .... Andalucía .... +34 958 32 18 61

La Almoraima Hotel .... Andalucía .... +34 956 693 002

La Casa Noble .... Andalucía .... +34 959 127 778

Vincci Selección Estrella del Mar .... Andalucía .... +34 951 053 970

Vincci Selección Posada del Patio .... Andalucía .... +34 951 001 020

Cas Gasi .... Balearic Islands .... +34 971 197 700

Gran Hotel Son Net .... Balearic Islands .... +34 971 14 70 00

Hotel Aimia .... Balearic Islands .... +34 971 631 200

Hotel Sant Joan de Binissaida .... Balearic Islands .... +34 971 35 55 98

PURAVIDA Resort Blau PortoPetro .... Balearic Islands .... +34 971 648 282

Son Granot .... Balearic Islands .... +34 971 355 555

Gran Hotel Atlantis Bahía Real .... Canary Islands .... +34 928 53 64 44

Gran Hotel Bahía del Duque Resort .... Canary Islands .... +34 922 746 932

Hotel Botánico & The Oriental Spa Garden .... Canary Islands .... +34 922 38 14 00

Vincci Selección La Plantacion del Sur .... Canary Islands .... +34 922 717 773

Hacienda Zorita Wine Hotel & Spa .... Castilla y León .... +34 923 129 400

Dolce Sitges .... Cataluña .... +34 938 109 000

Hotel 1898 .... Cataluña .... +34 93 552 95 52

Hotel Duquesa de Cardona .... Cataluña .... +34 93 268 90 90

Hotel Guitart Monterrey .... Cataluña .... +34 972 34 60 54

Hotel Rigat Park & Spa Beach Hotel .... Cataluña .... +34 972 36 52 00

Hotel Santa Marta .... Cataluña .... +34 972 364 904

Hotel Etxegana .... País Vasco .... +34 946 338 448

Barceló Asia Gardens Hotel & Thai Spa .... Valencia .... +34 966 818 400

El Rodat Hotel .... Valencia .... +34 966 470 710

Hotel Termas Marinas el Palasiet .... Valencia .... +34 964 300 250

Switzerland

Hotel Guarda Golf .... Crans~Montana .... +41 27 486 2000

Villa Orselina .... Locarno - Orselina .... +41 91 735 73 73

Elysian Collection .... Zermatt & Klosters .... +353 1 524 13 14

Turkey

Cornelia Diamond Golf Resort and Spa .... Antalya .... +90 242 710 1600

4reasons hotel+bistro .... Bodrum .... +90 252 385 3212

Casa Dell'Arte Residence .... Bodrum .... +90 252 367 1848

Kempinski Hotel Barbaros Bay .... Bodrum .... +90 252 311 03 03

Argos in Cappadocia .... Cappadocia - Uçhisar .... +90 384 2193130

Taskonaklar Hotel Cappadocia .... Cappadocia - Uçhisar .... +90 384 219 3001

Sacred House .... Cappadocia - Ürgüp .... +90 384 341 7102

A'jia Hotel .... Istanbul .... +90 216 413 9300

Sumahan On The Water .... Istanbul .... +90 216 422 8000

Villa Mahal .... Kalkan .... +90 242 844 32 68

Golden Key Bördübet .... Marmaris .... +90 252 436 92 30

WILLIS & GAMBIER
Furniture designed for life
CONDÉ NAST JOHANSENS
J
PREFERRED PARTNER
Because life is about choices
With a stunning portfolio of designs including, contemporary, classic French and rustic designs, Condé Nast Johansens preferred furniture supplier, Willis and Gambier, manufacture furniture that will add style and character to any setting
Visit www.wguk.com and be inspired!
www.wguk.com +44 (0) 1733 318400

Hotels - The Americas

Properties listed below can be found in our Recommended Hotels, Inns, Resorts, Spas & Villas – The Americas, Caribbean & Pacific 2013 Guide

CANADA - BRITISH COLUMBIA (SOOKE)

Sooke Harbour House

1528 Whiffen Spit Road, Sooke, British Columbia V9Z 0T4

Tel: +1 250 642 3421
www.condenastjohansens.com/sookeharbour

CANADA - BRITISH COLUMBIA (TOFINO)

Clayoquot Wilderness Resort

P.O. Box 130, Tofino, British Columbia V0R 2Z0

Tel: +1 250 726 8235
www.condenastjohansens.com/clayoquot

CANADA - BRITISH COLUMBIA (TOFINO)

Wickaninnish Inn

Osprey Lane at Chesterman Beach, Tofino, British Columbia V0R 2Z0

Tel: +1 250 725 3100
www.condenastjohansens.com/wickaninnish

CANADA - BRITISH COLUMBIA (VANCOUVER)

Wedgewood Hotel & Spa

845 Hornby Street, Vancouver, British Columbia V6Z 1V1

Tel: +1 604 689 7777
www.condenastjohansens.com/wedgewoodbc

CANADA - BRITISH COLUMBIA (VICTORIA)

The Magnolia Hotel & Spa

623 Courtney Street, Victoria, British Columbia V8W 1B8

Tel: +1 250 381 0999
www.condenastjohansens.com/magnoliahotel

CANADA - NOVA SCOTIA (EAST KEMPTVILLE)

Trout Point Lodge of Nova Scotia

189 Trout Point Road, Off the East Branch Road and Highway 203, East Kemptville, Nova Scotia B0W 1Y0

Tel: +1 902 761 2142
www.condenastjohansens.com/troutpoint

CANADA - ONTARIO (NIAGARA-ON-THE-LAKE)

Harbour House

85 Melville Street, Box 760, Niagara-on-the-Lake, Ontario L0S 1J0

Tel: +1 905 468 4683
www.condenastjohansens.com/harbourhouseca

CANADA - ONTARIO (TORONTO)

Windsor Arms

18 St. Thomas Street, Toronto, Ontario M5S 3E7

Tel: +1 416 971 9666
www.condenastjohansens.com/windsorarms

CANADA - QUÉBEC (MONT-TREMBLANT)

Hôtel Quintessence

3004 chemin de la chapelle, Mont-Tremblant, Québec J8E 1E1

Tel: +1 819 425 3400
www.condenastjohansens.com/quintessence

MÉXICO - BAJA CALIFORNIA SUR (CABO SAN LUCAS)

Esperanza, an Auberge Resort

Km. 7 Carretera Transpeninsular, Punta Ballena, Cabo San Lucas, Baja California Sur 23410

Tel: +52 624 145 6400
www.condenastjohansens.com/esperanza

MÉXICO - CHIAPAS (SAN CRISTOBAL DE LAS CASAS)

Hotel Bö

Av. 5 de Mayo 38, San Cristobal de las Casas, Chiapas 29240

Tel: +52 967 678 1515
www.condenastjohansens.com/hotelbo

MÉXICO - GUANAJUATO (GUANAJUATO)

Villa Maria Cristina

Paseo de La Presa de la Olla No. 76 Centro, Guanajuato, Guanajuato 36000

Tel: +52 473 731 2182
www.condenastjohansens.com/villamariacristina

MÉXICO - GUERRERO (ACAPULCO)

Las Brisas Acapulco

Carretera Escenica 5255, Acapulco, Guerrero 39867

Tel: +52 744 469 6900
www.condenastjohansens.com/brisasacapulco

Hotels - The Americas

Properties listed below can be found in our Recommended Hotels, Inns, Resorts, Spas & Villas – The Americas, Caribbean & Pacific 2013 Guide

MÉXICO - GUERRERO (IXTAPA - ZIHUATANEJO)

Loma Del Mar Thalasso Medical Spa & Resort

Ixtapa - Zihuatanejo, Guerrero 40884

Tel: +52 755 555 0460
www.condenastjohansens.com/lomadelmar

MÉXICO - MORELOS (TEPOZTLÁN)

Hostal de La Luz

Carretera Federal Tepoztlán, Amatlan Km. 4, Tepoztlán, Morelos 62524

Tel: +1 739 393 3076
www.condenastjohansens.com/hostaldelaluz

MÉXICO - JALISCO (COSTALEGRE - PUERTO VALLARTA)

Hotelito Desconocido Sanctuary Reserve & Spa

Playon de Mismaloya S/N, Municipio de Tomatlán, La Cruz de Loreto, Jalisco 48460

Tel: +52 322 281 4010
www.condenastjohansens.com/hotelito

MÉXICO - OAXACA (OAXACA)

Azul de Oaxaca Hotel + Galeria

Abasolo 313, Centro, 68000 Oaxaca, Oaxaca

Tel: +52 951 501 0016
www.condenastjohansens.com/hotelazuloaxaca

MÉXICO - JALISCO (COSTALEGRE - PUERTO VALLARTA)

Las Alamandas Resort

Carretera Barra de Navidad - Puerto Vallarta km 83.5, Col. Quemaro, Jalisco 48850

Tel: +52 322 285 5500
www.condenastjohansens.com/alamandas

MÉXICO - QUINTANA ROO (ISLA HOLBOX)

Casa Sandra

Calle de la Igualdad, Lázaro Cárdenas, Isla Holbox, Quintana Roo 77310

Tel: +52 984 875 2171
www.condenastjohansens.com/casasandra

MÉXICO - JALISCO (JOCOTEPEC)

El Chante Spa Hotel

Rivera del Lago 170-1, El Chante, Jocotepec, Jalisco 45825

Tel: +52 387 763 26 08
www.condenastjohansens.com/elchantespa

MÉXICO - YUCATÁN (MÉRIDA)

Hacienda Xcanatún - Casa de Piedra

Calle 20 S/N, Comisaría Xcanatún, Km. 12 Carretera Mérida - Progreso, Mérida, Yucatán 97302

Tel: +52 999 930 2140
www.condenastjohansens.com/xcanatun

MÉXICO - JALISCO (PUERTO VALLARTA)

Garza Blanca Preserve Resort & Spa

Km. 7.5 Carretera a Barra de Navidad, Puerto Vallarta, Jalisco 48390

Tel: +52 322 176 0700
www.condenastjohansens.com/garzablancaresort

U.S.A. - ARIZONA (GREER)

Hidden Meadow Ranch

620 County Road 1325, Greer, Arizona 85927

Tel: +1 928 333 1000
www.condenastjohansens.com/hiddenmeadow

MÉXICO - MÉXICO (VALLE DE BRAVO)

Hotel Rodavento

Km.3.5 Carretera Valle de Bravo -Los Saucos, Valle de Bravo, México 51200

Tel: +52 726 251 4182
www.condenastjohansens.com/rodavento

U.S.A. - ARIZONA (PARADISE VALLEY)

The Hermosa Inn

5532 North Palo Cristi Road, Paradise Valley, Arizona 85253

Tel: +1 602 955 8614
www.condenastjohansens.com/hermosa

MÉXICO - MORELOS (CUERNAVACA)

Anticavilla Hotel, Restaurante & Spa

Rio Amacuzac No. 10, Esquina Chilpancingo, Col. Vista Hermosa, Cuernavaca, Morelos 62290

Tel: +52 777 313 3131
www.condenastjohansens.com/anticavillahotel

U.S.A. - ARIZONA (PARADISE VALLEY - SCOTTSDALE)

Sanctuary on Camelback Mountain

5700 East McDonald Drive, Scottsdale, Arizona 85253

Tel: +1 480 948 2100
www.condenastjohansens.com/sanctuaryaz

MÉXICO - MORELOS (CUERNAVACA)

Las Mañanitas Hotel, Garden Restaurant & Spa

Ricardo Linares 107, Centro 62000, Cuernavaca, Morelos

Tel: +52 777 362 00 00
www.condenastjohansens.com/lasmananitas

U.S.A. - ARIZONA (TUBAC)

Tubac Golf Resort & Spa

One Otero Road, Tubac, Arizona 85646

Tel: +1 520 398 2211
www.condenastjohansens.com/tubac

Hotels - The Americas

Properties listed below can be found in our Recommended Hotels, Inns, Resorts, Spas & Villas – The Americas, Caribbean & Pacific 2013 Guide

U.S.A. - ARIZONA (TUCSON)

Hacienda del Sol Guest Ranch Resort

5501 N. Hacienda del Sol Road, Tucson, Arizona 85718

Tel: +1 520 299 1501
www.condenastjohansens.com/haciendadelsol

U.S.A. - ARIZONA (TUCSON)

Tanque Verde Ranch

14301 East Speedway Boulevard, Tucson, Arizona 85748

Tel: +1 520 296 6275
www.condenastjohansens.com/tanqueverde

U.S.A. - CALIFORNIA (BEVERLY HILLS)

Luxe Rodeo Drive Hotel

360 North Rodeo Drive, Beverly Hills, California 90210

Tel: +1 310 273 0300
www.condenastjohansens.com/luxerodeo

U.S.A. - CALIFORNIA (BIG SUR)

Post Ranch Inn

47900 Highway 1, Big Sur, California 93920

Tel: +1 831 667 2200
www.condenastjohansens.com/postranchinn

U.S.A. - CALIFORNIA (CALISTOGA)

The Chanric Inn

1805 Foothill Boulevard, Calistoga, California 94515

Tel: +1 707 942 4535
www.condenastjohansens.com/chanricinn

U.S.A. - CALIFORNIA (CARMEL-BY-THE-SEA)

L'Auberge Carmel

Monte Verde at Seventh, Carmel-by-the-Sea, California 93921

Tel: +1 831 624 8578
www.condenastjohansens.com/laubergecarmel

U.S.A. - CALIFORNIA (CARMEL-BY-THE-SEA)

Tradewinds Carmel

Mission Street at Third Avenue, Carmel-by-the-Sea, California 93921

Tel: +1 831 624 2776
www.condenastjohansens.com/tradewinds

U.S.A. - CALIFORNIA (CARMEL VALLEY)

Bernardus Lodge

415 West Carmel Valley Road, Carmel Valley, California 93924

Tel: +1 831 658 3400
www.condenastjohansens.com/bernardus

U.S.A. - CALIFORNIA (HEALDSBURG)

Hotel Les Mars

27 North Street, Healdsburg, California 95448

Tel: +1 707 433 4211
www.condenastjohansens.com/lesmarshotel

U.S.A. - CALIFORNIA (LAKE TAHOE)

PlumpJack Squaw Valley Inn

1920 Squaw Valley Road, Olympic Valley, California 96146

Tel: +1 530 583 1576
www.condenastjohansens.com/plumpjack

U.S.A. - CALIFORNIA (MENDOCINO)

The Stanford Inn By The Sea

Coast Highway One & Comptche-Ukiah Road, Mendocino, California 95460

Tel: +1 707 937 5615
www.condenastjohansens.com/stanfordinn

U.S.A. - CALIFORNIA (MONTEREY)

Old Monterey Inn

500 Martin Street, Monterey, California 93940

Tel: +1 831 375 8284
www.condenastjohansens.com/oldmontereyinn

U.S.A. - CALIFORNIA (NAPA)

Milliken Creek Inn & Spa

1815 Silverado Trail, Napa, California 94558

Tel: +1 707 255 1197
www.condenastjohansens.com/milliken

U.S.A. - CALIFORNIA (SAN FRANCISCO BAY AREA)

Inn Above Tide

30 El Portal, Sausalito, California 94965

Tel: +1 415 332 9535
www.condenastjohansens.com/innabovetide

U.S.A. - CALIFORNIA (SANTA MONICA)

Hotel Shangri-La

1301 Ocean Avenue, Santa Monica, California 90401

Tel: +1 310 394 2791
www.condenastjohansens.com/shangrilaca

U.S.A. - CALIFORNIA (YOUNTVILLE)

Bardessono

6526 Yount Street, Yountville, California 94599

Tel: +1 707 204 6000
www.condenastjohansens.com/bardessono

Hotels - The Americas

Properties listed below can be found in our Recommended Hotels, Inns, Resorts, Spas & Villas – The Americas, Caribbean & Pacific 2013 Guide

U.S.A. - COLORADO (DENVER)

Castle Marne Bed & Breakfast Inn

1572 Race Street, Denver, Colorado 80206

Tel: +1 303 331 0621
www.condenastjohansens.com/castlemarne

U.S.A. - COLORADO (ESTES PARK)

Taharaa Mountain Lodge

P.O. Box 2586, 3110 So. St. Vrain, Estes Park, Colorado 80517

Tel: +1 970 577 0098
www.condenastjohansens.com/taharaa

U.S.A. - COLORADO (STEAMBOAT SPRINGS)

Vista Verde Guest Ranch

P.O. Box 770465, Steamboat Springs, Colorado 80477

Tel: +1 970 879 3858
www.condenastjohansens.com/vistaverderanch

U.S.A. - COLORADO (TELLURIDE)

Hotel Columbia

301 West San Juan Avenue, Telluride, Colorado 81435

Tel: +1 970 728 0660/6294
www.condenastjohansens.com/columbiatelluride

U.S.A. - COLORADO (TELLURIDE)

lumiére Telluride

118 Lost Creek Lane, Telluride, Colorado 81435

Tel: +1 970 369 0400
www.condenastjohansens.com/lumiere

U.S.A. - COLORADO (VAIL)

Vail Mountain Lodge & Spa

352 East Meadow Drive, Vail, Colorado 81657

Tel: +1 970 476 0700
www.condenastjohansens.com/vailmountain

U.S.A. - CONNECTICUT (EAST HADDAM)

The Boardman House Inn

8 Norwich Road, East Haddam, Connecticut 06423

Tel: +1 860 873 9233
www.condenastjohansens.com/boardmanhouse

U.S.A. - DELAWARE (REHOBOTH BEACH)

Boardwalk Plaza Hotel

Olive Avenue & The Boardwalk, Rehoboth Beach, Delaware 19971

Tel: +1 302 227 7169
www.condenastjohansens.com/boardwalkplaza

U.S.A. - DELAWARE (WILMINGTON)

Inn at Montchanin Village & Spa

Route 100 & Kirk Road, Montchanin, Wilmington, Delaware 19710

Tel: +1 302 888 2133
www.condenastjohansens.com/montchanin

U.S.A. - DISTRICT OF COLUMBIA (WASHINGTON D.C.)

The Hay-Adams

Sixteenth & H. Streets N.W., Washington D.C., District of Columbia 20006

Tel: +1 202 638 6600
www.condenastjohansens.com/hayadams

U.S.A. - FLORIDA (AMELIA ISLAND)

Elizabeth Pointe Lodge

98 South Fletcher Avenue, Amelia Island, Florida 32034

Tel: +1 904 277 4851
www.condenastjohansens.com/elizabethpointelodge

U.S.A. - FLORIDA (AMELIA ISLAND)

Fairbanks House

227 South 7th Street, Amelia Island, Florida 32034

Tel: +1 904 277 0500
www.condenastjohansens.com/fairbankshouse

U.S.A. - FLORIDA (ATLANTIC BEACH)

One Ocean Resort & Spa

One Ocean Boulevard, Atlantic Beach, Florida 32233

Tel: +1 904 249 7402
www.condenastjohansens.com/oneoceanresort

U.S.A. - FLORIDA (BAL HARBOUR, MIAMI BEACH)

ONE Bal Harbour Resort & Spa

10295 Collins Avenue, Bal Harbour, Florida 33154

Tel: +1 305 455 5400
www.condenastjohansens.com/onebalharbour

U.S.A. - FLORIDA (FISHER ISLAND)

Fisher Island Hotel and Resort

One Fisher Island Drive, Fisher Island, Florida 33109

Tel: +1 305 535 6000
www.condenastjohansens.com/fisherisland

U.S.A. - FLORIDA (FORT LAUDERDALE)

The Pillars Hotel

111 North Birch Road, Fort Lauderdale, Florida 33304

Tel: +1 954 467 9639
www.condenastjohansens.com/pillarshotel

Hotels - The Americas

Properties listed below can be found in our Recommended Hotels, Inns, Resorts, Spas & Villas – The Americas, Caribbean & Pacific 2013 Guide

U.S.A. - FLORIDA (FORT LAUDERDALE)

The Pillars Villa

111 North Birch Road, Fort Lauderdale, Florida 33304

Tel: +1 954 467 9639
www.condenastjohansens.com/pillarsvilla

U.S.A. - FLORIDA (MIAMI BEACH)

The Betsy

1440 Ocean Drive, Miami Beach, Florida 33139

Tel: +1 305 531 6100
www.condenastjohansens.com/thebetsyhotel

U.S.A. - GEORGIA (CUMBERLAND ISLAND)

Greyfield Inn

Cumberland Island, Georgia

Tel: +1 904 261 6408
www.condenastjohansens.com/greyfieldinn

U.S.A. - ILLINOIS (CHICAGO)

Trump International Hotel & Tower® Chicago

401 North Wabash Avenue, Chicago, Illinois 60611

Tel: +1 312 588 8000
www.condenastjohansens.com/trumpchicago

U.S.A. - MAINE (KENNEBUNK BEACH)

The White Barn Inn & Spa

37 Beach Avenue, Kennebunk Beach, Maine 04043

Tel: +1 207 967 2321
www.condenastjohansens.com/whitebarninn

U.S.A. - MAINE (PORTLAND)

Portland Harbor Hotel

468 Fore Street, Portland, Maine 04101

Tel: +1 207 775 9090
www.condenastjohansens.com/portlandharbor

U.S.A. - MASSACHUSETTS (BOSTON)

Boston Harbor Hotel

70 Rowes Wharf, Boston, Massachusetts 02110

Tel: +1 617 439 7000
www.condenastjohansens.com/bhh

U.S.A. - MASSACHUSETTS (BOSTON)

Fifteen Beacon

15 Beacon Street, Boston, Massachusetts 02108

Tel: +1 617 670 1500
www.condenastjohansens.com/xvbeacon

U.S.A. - MASSACHUSETTS (BOSTON)

Revere Hotel

200 Stuart Street, Boston, Massachusetts 02116

Tel: +1 617 482 1800
www.condenastjohansens.com/reverehotel

U.S.A. - MASSACHUSETTS (CAMBRIDGE)

The Hotel Veritas

One Remington Street in Harvard Square, Cambridge, Massachusetts 02138

Tel: +1 617 520 5000
www.condenastjohansens.com/thehotelveritas

U.S.A. - MASSACHUSETTS (CAPE COD)

Wequassett Resort and Golf Club

On Pleasant Bay, Chatham, Massachusetts 02633

Tel: +1 508 432 5400
www.condenastjohansens.com/wequassett

U.S.A. - MASSACHUSETTS (IPSWICH)

The Inn at Castle Hill

280 Argilla Road, Ipswich, Massachusetts 01938

Tel: +1 978 412 2555
www.condenastjohansens.com/castlehill

U.S.A. - MASSACHUSETTS (LENOX)

Blantyre

16 Blantyre Road, P.O. Box 995, Lenox, Massachusetts 01240

Tel: +1 413 637 3556
www.condenastjohansens.com/blantyre

U.S.A. - MONTANA (DARBY)

Triple Creek Ranch

5551 West Fork Road, Darby, Montana 59829

Tel: +1 406 821 4600
www.condenastjohansens.com/triplecreek

U.S.A. - NEVADA (LAS VEGAS)

SKYLOFTS at MGM Grand

3799 Las Vegas Boulevard South, Las Vegas, Nevada 89109

Tel: +1 702 891 6098
www.condenastjohansens.com/skylofts

U.S.A. - NEW MEXICO (SANTA FE)

The Hacienda at Hotel Santa Fe

1501 Paseo de Peralta, Santa Fe, New Mexico 87501

Tel: +1 505 982 1200
www.condenastjohansens.com/hotelsantafe

Hotels - The Americas

Properties listed below can be found in our Recommended Hotels, Inns, Resorts, Spas & Villas – The Americas, Caribbean & Pacific 2013 Guide

U.S.A. - NEW YORK (NEW YORK CITY)

The Inn at Irving Place

56 Irving Place, New York, New York City 10003

Tel: +1 212 533 4600
www.condenastjohansens.com/irving

U.S.A. - NEW YORK (NEW YORK CITY)

Trump International Hotel & Tower®

One Central Park West, New York City, New York 10023

Tel: +1 212 299 1000
www.condenastjohansens.com/trumpnewyork

U.S.A. - NEW YORK (VERONA)

The Lodge at Turning Stone

5218 Patrick Road, Verona, New York 13478

Tel: +1 315 361 8525
www.condenastjohansens.com/turningstone

U.S.A. - NEW YORK/LONG ISLAND (EAST HAMPTON)

The Baker House 1650

181 Main Street, East Hampton, New York 11937

Tel: +1 631 324 4081
www.condenastjohansens.com/bakerhouse

U.S.A. - NORTH CAROLINA (HIGHLANDS)

Inn at Half Mile Farm

P.O. Box 2769, 214 Half Mile Drive, Highlands, North Carolina 28741

Tel: +1 828 526 8170
www.condenastjohansens.com/halfmilefarm

U.S.A. - SOUTH CAROLINA (CHARLESTON)

Charleston Harbor Resort & Marina

20 Patriots Point Road, Charleston, South Carolina 29464

Tel: +1 843 856 0028
www.condenastjohansens.com/charlestonharbor

U.S.A. - VIRGINIA (MIDDLEBURG)

Goodstone Inn & Restaurant

36205 Snake Hill Road, Middleburg, Virginia 20117

Tel: +1 540 687 3333
www.condenastjohansens.com/goodstoneinn

U.S.A. - WASHINGTON (BELLEVUE)

Hotel Bellevue

11200 S.E. 6th Street, Bellevue, Washington 98004

Tel: +1 425 454 4424 and +1 425 455 1616
www.condenastjohansens.com/bellevue

U.S.A. - WASHINGTON (SPOKANE)

The Davenport Hotel and Tower

10 South Post Street, Spokane, Washington 99201

Tel: +1 509 455 8888
www.condenastjohansens.com/davenport

U.S.A. - WASHINGTON (SPOKANE)

Hotel Lusso

808 West Sprague Avenue, Spokane, Washington 99201

Tel: +1 509 747 9750
www.condenastjohansens.com/hotellusso

U.S.A. - WYOMING (SARATOGA)

The Lodge and Spa at Brush Creek Ranch

66 Brush Creek Ranch Road, Saratoga, Wyoming 82331

Tel: +1 307 327 5284
www.condenastjohansens.com/brushcreekranch

BELIZE - AMBERGRIS CAYE (CAYO ESPANTO)

Cayo Espanto a private island

Ambergris Caye, Cayo Espanto

Tel: +910 323 8355
www.condenastjohansens.com/cayoespanto

BELIZE - AMBERGRIS CAYE (NEAR SAN PEDRO)

Matachica Resort & Spa

5 miles North of San Pedro, Ambergris Caye

Tel: +501 226 5010/1
www.condenastjohansens.com/matachica

BELIZE - AMBERGRIS CAYE (SAN PEDRO)

The Phoenix Resort

P.O. Box 25, San Pedro, Ambergris Caye

Tel: +501 226 2083
www.condenastjohansens.com/thephoenixbelize

BELIZE - AMBERGRIS CAYE (SAN PEDRO)

Victoria House

P.O. Box 22, San Pedro, Ambergris Caye

Tel: +501 226 2067
www.condenastjohansens.com/victoriahouse

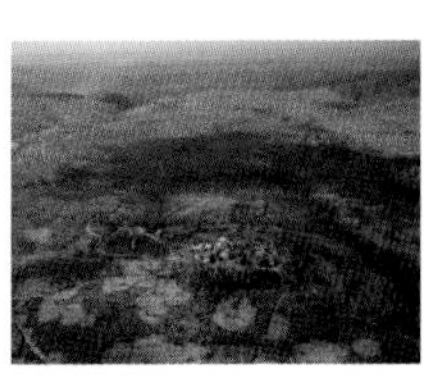

BELIZE - CAYO DISTRICT (MOUNTAIN PINE RIDGE FOREST RESERVE)

Hidden Valley Inn

P.O. Box 170, Belmopan

Tel: +501 822 3320
www.condenastjohansens.com/hiddenvalleyinn

Hotels - The Americas

Properties listed below can be found in our Recommended Hotels, Inns, Resorts, Spas & Villas – The Americas, Caribbean & Pacific 2013 Guide

BELIZE - CAYO DISTRICT (SAN IGNACIO)

The Lodge at Chaa Creek

P.O. Box 53, San Ignacio, Cayo District

Tel: +501 824 2037
www.condenastjohansens.com/chaacreek

BELIZE - TOLEDO DISTRICT (PUNTA GORDA)

Belcampo Lodge Belize

P.O. Box 135, Punta Gorda, Toledo District

Tel: +501 722 0050
www.condenastjohansens.com/belcampo

COSTA RICA - ALAJUELA (LA FORTUNA DE SAN CARLOS)

Tabacón Grand Spa Thermal Resort

La Fortuna de San Carlos, Arenal

Tel: +506 2519 1900
www.condenastjohansens.com/tabacon

COSTA RICA - GUANACASTE (PINILLA)

La Posada Inn

Hacienda Pinilla, Pinilla, Guanacaste

Tel: +506 2680 3000
www.condenastjohansens.com/laposadapinilla

COSTA RICA - LIMÓN (PUERTO VIEJO)

Le Caméléon

Cocles Beach, Puerto Viejo, Limón

Tel: +506 2750 0501
www.condenastjohansens.com/lecameleon

COSTA RICA - PUNTARENAS (MANUEL ANTONIO)

Casa Reserva

La Reserva, Manuel Antonio

Tel: +506 2777 7979
www.condenastjohansens.com/casareserva

COSTA RICA - PUNTARENAS (MANUEL ANTONIO)

Gaia Hotel & Reserve

Km 2.7 Carretera Quepos, Manuel Antonio, Puntarenas

Tel: +506 2777 9797
www.condenastjohansens.com/gaiahr

COSTA RICA - PUNTARENAS (PLAYA ESTERILLOS ESTE)

Alma del Pacifico Hotel

Playa Esterillos Este, Puntarenas

Tel: +506 2778 7070
www.condenastjohansens.com/delpacifico

GUATEMALA - SACATEPÉQUEZ (LA ANTIGUA GUATEMALA)

Casa Quinta Hotel Boutique

5 Av. Sur No. 45, La Antigua Guatemala, Sacatepéquez

Tel: +502 7832 6181
www.condenastjohansens.com/hotelcasaquinta

GUATEMALA - SACATEPÉQUEZ (LA ANTIGUA GUATEMALA)

El Convento Boutique Hotel Antigua Guatemala

2a Avenue Norte 11, La Antigua Guatemala, Sacatepéquez

Tel: +502 7720 7272
www.condenastjohansens.com/elconventoantigua

GUATEMALA - SACATEPÉQUEZ (SAN JUAN ALOTENANGO - LA ANTIGUA GUATEMALA)

La Reunión Golf Resort & Residences

Km. 91.5 Ruta Nacional 14, San Juan Alotenango, Sacatepéquez

Tel: +502 7873 1400
www.condenastjohansens.com/lareunion

ARGENTINA - BUENOS AIRES (CIUDAD DE BUENOS AIRES)

Algodon Mansion

Montevideo 1647, Ciudad de Buenos Aires, Buenos Aires

Tel: +54 11 3530 7777
www.condenastjohansens.com/algodonmansion

ARGENTINA - BUENOS AIRES (CIUDAD DE BUENOS AIRES)

BA Sohotel

Paraguay 4485, 1425 Ciudad de Buenos Aires, Buenos Aires

Tel: +54 11 4832 4474
www.condenastjohansens.com/basohotel

ARGENTINA - BUENOS AIRES (CIUDAD DE BUENOS AIRES)

Legado Mitico

Gurruchaga 1848, C1414DIL Ciudad de Buenos Aires, Buenos Aires

Tel: +54 11 4833 1300
www.condenastjohansens.com/legadomitico

ARGENTINA - BUENOS AIRES (CIUDAD DE BUENOS AIRES)

Mine Hotel Boutique

Gorriti 4770, Palermo Soho, C1414BJL Ciudad de Buenos Aires, Buenos Aires

Tel: +54 11 4832 1100
www.condenastjohansens.com/minehotel

ARGENTINA - BUENOS AIRES (EZEIZA)

Estancia Villa María

Av. Pereda s/n, Máximo Paz, Ezeiza, Buenos Aires

Tel: +54 11 4815 0989
www.condenastjohansens.com/estanciavillamaria

Hotels - The Americas

Properties listed below can be found in our Recommended Hotels, Inns, Resorts, Spas & Villas – The Americas, Caribbean & Pacific 2013 Guide

ARGENTINA - BUENOS AIRES (LOBOS)

Estancia La Candelaria

Ruta Nacional 205, km 114.5, Lobos, Buenos Aires

Tel: +54 2227 424404/494132/494473
www.condenastjohansens.com/estanciacandelaria

ARGENTINA - BUENOS AIRES (SAN ISIDRO)

Hotel Del Casco

Avenida del Libertador 16,170, B1642CKV, San Isidro, Buenos Aires

Tel: +54 11 4732 3993
www.condenastjohansens.com/hoteldelcasco

ARGENTINA - NEUQUÉN (PATAGONIA - VILLA LA ANGOSTURA)

Las Balsas Gourmet Hotel & Spa

Bahía Las Balsas s/n, 8407 Villa La Angostura, Neuquén

Tel: +54 2944 494308
www.condenastjohansens.com/lasbalsas

ARGENTINA - RÍO NEGRO (PATAGONIA - SAN CARLOS DE BARILOCHE)

Llao Llao Hotel & Resort, Golf-Spa

Av. Ezequiel Bustillo Km 25, San Carlos de Bariloche, Río Negro, Patagonia

Tel: +54 294 444 8530
www.condenastjohansens.com/llaollao

BRAZIL - ALAGOAS (BARRA DE SÃO MIGUEL)

Kenoa - Exclusive Beach Spa & Resort

Rua Escritor Jorge Lima 58, Barra de São Miguel, Alagoas 57180-000

Tel: +55 82 3272 1285
www.condenastjohansens.com/kenoaresort

BRAZIL - ALAGOAS (PORTO DE PEDRAS)

Pousada Patacho

Praia do Patacho s/n, Porto de Pedras, Alagoas 57945-000

Tel: +55 82 3298 1253
www.condenastjohansens.com/pousadapatacho

BRAZIL - ALAGOAS (SÃO MIGUEL DOS MILAGRES)

Pousada do Toque

Rua Felisberto de Ataide, Povoado do Toque, São Miguel dos Milagres, Alagoas 57940-000

Tel: +55 82 3295 1127
www.condenastjohansens.com/pousadadotoque

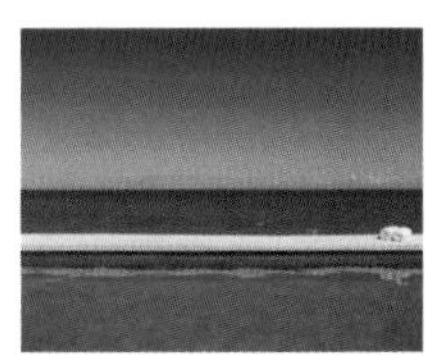

BRAZIL - BAHIA (ARRAIAL D'AJUDA)

Maitei Hotel

Estrada do Mucugê 475, Arraial D'Ajuda, Porto Seguro, Bahia 45816-000

Tel: +55 73 3575 3877
www.condenastjohansens.com/maitei

BRAZIL - BAHIA (CORUMBAU)

Fazenda São Francisco

Ponta do Corumbau s/n, Prado, Bahia

Tel: +55 11 3078 4411
www.condenastjohansens.com/fazenda

BRAZIL - BAHIA (ITACARÉ)

Txai Resort

Rod. Ilhéus-Itacaré km. 48, Itacaré, Bahia 45530-000

Tel: +55 73 2101 5000
www.condenastjohansens.com/txairesort

BRAZIL - BAHIA (PENÍNSULA DE MARAÚ - MARAÚ)

Kiaroa Eco-Luxury Resort

Loteamento da Costa, área SD6, Distrito de Barra Grande, Municipio de Maraú, Bahia, CEP 45 520-000

Tel: +55 73 3258 6214
www.condenastjohansens.com/kiaroa

BRAZIL - BAHIA (TRANCOSO)

Estrela D'Água

Estrada Arraial d'Ajuda/Trancoso, 1011, Trancoso Porto Seguro, Bahia 45818-000

Tel: +55 73 3668 1030
www.condenastjohansens.com/estreladagua

BRAZIL - BAHIA (TRANCOSO)

Etnia Clube de Mar

Estrada Trancoso, Itaquena No. 300, Km 02, Trancoso, Bahia 45818-000

Tel: +55 73 3668 1137
www.condenastjohansens.com/etniaclube

BRAZIL - BAHIA (TRANCOSO)

Etnia Pousada and Boutique

Trancoso, Bahia 45818-000

Tel: + 55 73 3668 1137
www.condenastjohansens.com/etnia

BRAZIL - CEARÁ (JERICOACOARA)

Vila Kalango

Rua das Dunas 30, Jericoacoara, Ceará 62598-000

Tel: +55 88 3669 2290
www.condenastjohansens.com/vilakalango

BRAZIL - MINAS GERAIS (LIMA DUARTE)

Reserva do Ibitipoca

Fazenda do Engenho, s/n Conceição do Ibitipoca, Lima Duarte, Minas Gerais 36140-000

Tel: +55 32 3281 8174
www.condenastjohansens.com/reservadoibitipoca

Hotels - The Americas

Properties listed below can be found in our Recommended Hotels, Inns, Resorts, Spas & Villas – The Americas, Caribbean & Pacific 2013 Guide

BRAZIL - MINAS GERAIS (TIRADENTES)

Solar da Ponte

Praça das Mercês S/N, Tiradentes, Minas Gerais 36325-000

Tel: +55 32 33 55 12 55
www.condenastjohansens.com/solardaponte

BRAZIL - PARANÁ (FOZ DO IGUAÇU)

Hotel das Cataratas

Rodovia BR. 469 KM. 32, Iguassu National Park, Foz do Iguaçu, Paraná 85853-000

Tel: +55 45 2102 7000
www.condenastjohansens.com/hoteldascataratas

BRAZIL - PARANÁ (LAPA)

Lapinha Spa

Estrada da Lapa, Rio Negro, Km 16, Lapa, Paraná 83750-000

Tel: +55 41 3622 1044
www.condenastjohansens.com/lapinha

BRAZIL - PERNAMBUCO (FERNANDO DE NORONHA)

Pousada Maravilha

Rodovia BR-363, s/n, Sueste, Ilha de Fernando de Noronha, Pernambuco 53990-000

Tel: +55 81 3619 0028/1290
www.condenastjohansens.com/maravilha

BRAZIL - PERNAMBUCO (PORTO DE GALINHAS)

Nannai Beach Resort

Rodovia PE-09, acesso à Muro Alto, Km 3, Ipojuca, Pernambuco 55590-000

Tel: +55 81 3552 0100
www.condenastjohansens.com/nannaibeach

BRAZIL - RIO DE JANEIRO (BÚZIOS)

Casas Brancas Boutique-Hotel & Spa

Alto do Humaitá 10, Armação dos Búzios, Rio de Janeiro 28950-000

Tel: +55 22 2623 1458
www.condenastjohansens.com/casasbrancas

BRAZIL - RIO DE JANEIRO (BÚZIOS)

Hotel Le Relais La Borie

1374 Rua dos Gravatás, Praia de Geribá, Armação dos Búzios, Rio de Janeiro 28950-000

Tel: +55 22 2620 8504
www.condenastjohansens.com/laborie

BRAZIL - RIO DE JANEIRO (BÚZIOS)

Insólito Boutique Hotel

Rua E1 - Lotes 3 and 4, Condomínio Atlântico, Armação de Búzios, Rio de Janeiro 28.950-000

Tel: +55 22 2623 2172
www.condenastjohansens.com/insolitohotel

BRAZIL - RIO DE JANEIRO (PETRÓPOLIS)

Solar do Império

Koeler Avenue, 376 Centro, Petrópolis, Rio de Janeiro

Tel: +55 24 2103 3000
www.condenastjohansens.com/solardoimperio

BRAZIL - RIO DE JANEIRO (PETRÓPOLIS)

Tankamana EcoResort

Estrada Júlio Cápua, S/N Vale Do Cuiabá, Itaipava - Petrópolis, Rio De Janeiro 25745-050

Tel: +55 24 2232 2900
www.condenastjohansens.com/tankamana

BRAZIL - RIO DE JANEIRO (RIO DE JANEIRO)

Copacabana Palace

Avenida Atlântica 1702, Rio de Janeiro, Rio de Janeiro 22021-001

Tel: +55 21 2548 7070
www.condenastjohansens.com/copacabanapalace

BRAZIL - RIO DE JANEIRO (RIO DE JANEIRO)

Hotel Marina All Suites

Av. Delfim Moreira 696, Praia do Leblon, Rio de Janeiro 22441-000

Tel: +55 21 2172 1001
www.condenastjohansens.com/marinaallsuites

BRAZIL - RIO GRANDE DO NORTE (PRAIA DA PIPA)

Toca da Coruja

Avenida Baia dos Golfinhos 464, Praia da Pipa, Tibau do Sul, Rio Grande do Norte 59178-000

Tel: +55 84 3246 2226
www.condenastjohansens.com/tocadacoruja

BRAZIL - RIO GRANDE DO SUL (GRAMADO)

Estalagem St. Hubertus

Rua Carrieri, 974, Gramado, Rio Grande do Sul 95670-000

Tel: +55 54 3286 1273
www.condenastjohansens.com/sthubertus

BRAZIL - RIO GRANDE DO SUL (GRAMADO)

Kurotel Medical Longevity Center and Spa

Rua Nacões Unidas 533, P.O. Box 65, Gramado, Rio Grande do Sul 95670-000

Tel: +55 54 3295 9393
www.condenastjohansens.com/kurotel

BRAZIL - RIO GRANDE DO SUL (GRAMADO)

La Hacienda Inn and Restaurant

Estrada da Serra Grande 4200, Gramado, Rio Grande do Sul 95670-000

Tel: +55 54 3295 3025
www.condenastjohansens.com/lahacienda

Hotels - The Americas

Properties listed below can be found in our Recommended Hotels, Inns, Resorts, Spas & Villas – The Americas, Caribbean & Pacific 2013 Guide

BRAZIL - RIO GRANDE DO SUL (GRAMADO)

Saint Andrews Gramado

Rua das Flores 171, Vale do BoSque, Gramado, Rio Grande do Sul 95670-000

Tel: +55 54 3295 7700
www.condenastjohansens.com/saintandrews

BRAZIL - RIO GRANDE DO SUL (GRAMADO)

Varanda das Bromélias Boutique Hotel

Rua Alarich Schulz, 198 Bairro Planalto, 95670-000 Gramado, Rio Grande do Sul

Tel: +55 54 3286 0547
www.condenastjohansens.com/varandadasbromelias

BRAZIL - SANTA CATARINA (GOVERNADOR CELSO RAMOS)

Ponta dos Ganchos

Rua Eupídio Alves do Nascimento 104, Governador Celso Ramos, Santa Catarina 88190-000

Tel: +55 48 3953 7000
www.condenastjohansens.com/pontadosganchos

BRAZIL - SANTA CATARINA (IMBITUBA)

Ponta da Piteira

Ibiraquera, Imbituba, Santa Catarina

Tel: +55 48 3356 0232
www.condenastjohansens.com/pontadapiteira

BRAZIL - SANTA CATARINA (PRAIA DO ROSA)

Pousada Solar Mirador

Estrada Geral do Rosa s/n, Praia do Rosa, Imbituba, Santa Catarina 88780-000

Tel: +55 48 3355 6144
www.condenastjohansens.com/solarmirador

BRAZIL - SÃO PAULO (AMPARO)

Hotel Sant'Anna

Fazenda Sant´Anna s/n Bairro Córrego Vermelho, Caixa Postal 81, Amparo, São Paulo 13900 470

Tel: +55 11 3509 4252
www.condenastjohansens.com/hotelsantanna

BRAZIL - SÃO PAULO (CAMPOS DO JORDÃO)

Hotel Frontenac

Av. Dr. Paulo Ribas, 295 Capivari, Campos do Jordão, São Paulo 12460-000

Tel: +55 12 3669 1000
www.condenastjohansens.com/frontenac

BRAZIL - SÃO PAULO (CAMPOS DO JORDÃO)

Hotel Toriba

Avenida Ernesto Diederichsen 2962, Campos do Jordão, São Paulo 12460-000

Tel: +55 12 3668 5000
www.condenastjohansens.com/toriba

BRAZIL - SÃO PAULO (ILHABELA)

DPNY Beach Hotel

Av. José Pacheco do Nascimento, 7668, Praia do Curral, Ilhabela, São Paulo 11630-000

Tel: +55 12 3894 3000
www.condenastjohansens.com/dpnybeach

BRAZIL - SÃO PAULO (SANTO ANTÔNIO DO PINHAL)

Pousada Quinta dos Pinhais

Estrada do Pico Agudo, KM. 3, Santo Antônio do Pinhal, São Paulo 12450-000

Tel: +55 12 3666 2030
www.condenastjohansens.com/quintadospinhais

BRAZIL - SÃO PAULO (SÃO PAULO)

Hotel Unique

Avenida Brigadeiro Luis Antonio, 4.700 São Paulo, São Paulo 01402-002

Tel: +55 11 3055 4710
www.condenastjohansens.com/hotelunique

BRAZIL - SÃO PAULO (SERRA DA CANTAREIRA)

Unique Garden Hotel & Spa

Estrada Laramara, 3500, Serra da Cantareira, São Paulo 07600-970

Tel: +55 11 4486 8700
www.condenastjohansens.com/uniquegarden

CHILE - X REGIÓN DE LOS LAGOS (PATAGONIA - PUERTO MONTT)

Nomads of the Seas

Puerto Montt, X Región de los Lagos

Tel: +562 414 4600
www.condenastjohansens.com/nomadsoftheseas

COLOMBIA - BOLÍVAR (CARTAGENA DE INDIAS)

Anandá Hotel Boutique

Calle del Cuartel N. 36-77, Cartagena de Indias, Bolívar

Tel: +57 5 664 4452
www.condenastjohansens.com/anandacartagena

COLOMBIA - BOLÍVAR (CARTAGENA DE INDIAS)

Bóvedas de Santa Clara Hotel Boutique

Calle del Torno No. 39-29, Barrio San Diego, Cartagena de Indias, Bolívar

Tel: +57 5 650 44 65
www.condenastjohansens.com/bovedasdesantaclara

COLOMBIA - BOLÍVAR (CARTAGENA DE INDIAS)

Casa Pestagua

Calle Santo Domingo No. 33-63, Cartagena de Indias, Bolívar

Tel: +57 5 664 9510/6286
www.condenastjohansens.com/casapestagua

Hotels - The Americas & Caribbean

Properties listed below can be found in our Recommended Hotels, Inns, Resorts, Spas & Villas – The Americas, Caribbean & Pacific 2013 Guide

COLOMBIA - BOLÍVAR (CARTAGENA DE INDIAS)

Hotel San Pedro de Majagua

Isla Grande, Islas del Rosario, Cartagena de Indias, Bolívar

Tel: +57 5 650 44 65
www.condenastjohansens.com/hotelmajagua

COLOMBIA - OICATÁ (PAIPA)

Hotel Spa Castillo del Viento

Km 8 Vía Tunja, Paipa, Oicatá

Tel: +57 3 118 096344
www.condenastjohansens.com/castillodelviento

ECUADOR - GALÁPAGOS ISLANDS (SANTA CRUZ ISLAND)

Royal Palm Hotel - Galápagos

Km. 18 Via Baltra, Santa Cruz Island, Galápagos Islands

Tel: +593 5 252 7408
www.condenastjohansens.com/royalpalmgalapagos

ECUADOR - IMBABURA (COTACACHI)

La Mirage Garden Hotel & Spa

Cotacachi, Imbabura

Tel: +593 6 291 5237
www.condenastjohansens.com/mirage

ECUADOR - IMBABURA (SAN PABLO DEL LAGO)

4 Volcanoes Lodge

Calle Sucre, San Pablo del Lago, Imbabura

Tel: +593 6 291 8488
www.condenastjohansens.com/4volcanoes

ECUADOR - PICHINCHA (QUITO)

Hotel Plaza Grande

Calle García Moreno, N5-16 y Chile, Pichincha, Quito

Tel: +593 2 2528 700
www.condenastjohansens.com/plazagrandequito

PERÚ - CUSCO (MACHU PICCHU PUEBLO)

Inkaterra Machu Picchu Pueblo Hotel

Machu Picchu Pueblo, Cusco

Tel: +51 1 610 0400
www.condenastjohansens.com/inkaterra

PERÚ - LIMA (LIMA)

Swissôtel Lima

Via Central 150, Centro Empresarial Real, San Isidro, Lima 27

Tel: +511 421 4400
www.condenastjohansens.com/swissotellima

PERÚ - LIMA (SANTIAGO DE VIÑAK)

Viñak - Sierra de Lunahuaná Lodge

Santiago de Viñak, Yauyos, Lima

Tel: +511 421 6952 Ext. 105
www.condenastjohansens.com/refugiosdelperu

URUGUAY - MALDONADO (JOSÉ IGNACIO)

Casa Suaya

Ruta 10 Km 185, 5, José Ignacio

Tel: +598 4486 2750
www.condenastjohansens.com/casasuaya

URUGUAY - MALDONADO (PUNTA DEL ESTE)

L'Auberge

Carnoustie y Av. del Agua, Barrio Parque del Golf, Punta del Este CP20100

Tel: +598 4248 8888
www.condenastjohansens.com/laubergeuruguay

CARIBBEAN - ANGUILLA (LITTLE BAY)

Àni Villas

Little Bay

Tel: +1 264 497 7888
www.condenastjohansens.com/anivillas

CARIBBEAN - ANGUILLA (MAUNDAYS BAY)

Cap Juluca

Maundays Bay, AI-2640

Tel: +1 264 497 6666
www.condenastjohansens.com/capjuluca

CARIBBEAN - ANGUILLA (RENDEZVOUS BAY)

CuisinArt Golf Resort & Spa

P.O. Box 2000, Rendezvous Bay

Tel: +1 264 498 2000
www.condenastjohansens.com/cuisinartresort

CARIBBEAN - ANGUILLA (SANDY HILL BAY BEACH)

Bird of Paradise

Sandy Hill Bay Beach

Tel: +1 414 791 9461
www.condenastjohansens.com/birdofparadise

CARIBBEAN - ANGUILLA (WEST END)

Sheriva Luxury Villas & Suites

Maundays Bay Road, West End AI-2640

Tel: +1 264 498 9898
www.condenastjohansens.com/sheriva

Hotels - Caribbean

Properties listed below can be found in our Recommended Hotels, Inns, Resorts, Spas & Villas – The Americas, Caribbean & Pacific 2013 Guide

CARIBBEAN - ANTIGUA (ST. JOHN'S)

Blue Waters

P.O. Box 257, St. John's

Tel: +44 870 360 1245
www.condenastjohansens.com/bluewaters

CARIBBEAN - ANTIGUA (ST. JOHN'S)

Curtain Bluff

P.O. Box 288, St. John's

Tel: +1 268 462 8400
www.condenastjohansens.com/curtainbluff

CARIBBEAN - ANTIGUA (ST. JOHN'S)

Galley Bay Resort & Spa

Five Islands, St. John's

Tel: +1 954 481 8787
www.condenastjohansens.com/galleybay

CARIBBEAN - ANTIGUA (ST. JOHN'S)

The Inn at English Harbour

P.O. Box 187, St. John's

Tel: +1 268 460 1014
www.condenastjohansens.com/innatenglishharbour

CARIBBEAN - BARBADOS (CHRIST CHURCH)

Little Arches

Enterprise Beach Road, Christ Church

Tel: +1 246 420 4689
www.condenastjohansens.com/littlearches

CARIBBEAN - BRITISH VIRGIN ISLANDS (PETER ISLAND)

Peter Island Resort and Spa

Peter Island

Tel: +616 458 6767
www.condenastjohansens.com/peterislandresort

CARIBBEAN - BRITISH VIRGIN ISLANDS (PETER ISLAND)

The Villas at Peter Island

Peter Island

Tel: +616 458 6767
www.condenastjohansens.com/villaspeterisland

CARIBBEAN - BRITISH VIRGIN ISLANDS (VIRGIN GORDA)

Biras Creek Resort

North Sound, Virgin Gorda

Tel: +1 284 494 3555
www.condenastjohansens.com/birascreek

CARIBBEAN - CAYMAN ISLANDS (GRAND CAYMAN)

Cotton Tree

375 Conch Point Road, P.O. Box 31324, Grand Cayman KY1-1206

Tel: +1 345 943 0700
www.condenastjohansens.com/caymancottontree

CARIBBEAN - GRENADA (ST. GEORGE'S)

LaSource

Pink Gin Beach, St. George's

Tel: +1 473 444 2556
www.condenastjohansens.com/lasource

CARIBBEAN - GRENADA (ST. GEORGE'S)

Spice Island Beach Resort

Grand Anse Beach, St. George's

Tel: +1 473 444 4258
www.condenastjohansens.com/spiceisland

CARIBBEAN - JAMAICA (MONTEGO BAY)

The Tryall Club

P.O. Box 1206, Montego Bay

Tel: +1 876 956 5660
www.condenastjohansens.com/tryallclub

CARIBBEAN - PUERTO RICO (CONDADO)

O:live Boutique Hotel

Aguadilla Street #55, Condado 00907

Tel: +1 787 705 9994
www.condenastjohansens.com/oliveboutiquehotel

CARIBBEAN - SAINT-BARTHÉLEMY (ANSE DE TOINY)

Hôtel Le Toiny

Anse de Toiny

Tel: +590 590 27 88 88
www.condenastjohansens.com/letoiny

CARIBBEAN - SAINT-BARTHÉLEMY (GRAND CUL DE SAC)

Hotel Guanahani & Spa

Grand Cul de Sac

Tel: +590 590 27 66 60
www.condenastjohansens.com/guanahani

CARIBBEAN - SAINT-MARTIN (BAIE LONGUE)

La Samanna

P.O. Box 4077, 97064 CEDEX

Tel: +590 590 87 64 00
www.condenastjohansens.com/lasamanna

Hotels - Caribbean

Properties listed below can be found in our Recommended Hotels, Inns, Resorts, Spas & Villas – The Americas, Caribbean & Pacific 2013 Guide

CARIBBEAN - ST. LUCIA (CAP ESTATE)

Cap Maison Resort & Spa

Smugglers Cove Drive, Cap Estate, Gros Islet

Tel: +1 758 457 8670
www.condenastjohansens.com/capmaison

CARIBBEAN - ST. LUCIA (SOUFRIÈRE)

Anse Chastanet

Soufrière

Tel: +1 758 459 7000
www.condenastjohansens.com/ansechastanet

CARIBBEAN - ST. LUCIA (SOUFRIÈRE)

Boucan by Hotel Chocolat

The Rabot Estate, P.O. Box 312, Soufrière

Tel: +44 844 544 1272
www.condenastjohansens.com/hotelchocolat

CARIBBEAN - ST. LUCIA (SOUFRIÈRE)

Jade Mountain at Anse Chastanet

Soufrière

Tel: +1 758 459 4000
www.condenastjohansens.com/jademountain

CARIBBEAN - ST. LUCIA (SOUFRIÈRE)

Ladera

Soufrière

Tel: 0800 097 3501
www.condenastjohansens.com/ladera

CARIBBEAN - THE GRENADINES (MUSTIQUE ISLAND)

Cotton House

P.O. Box 349, Mustique Island

Tel: +1 784 456 4777
www.condenastjohansens.com/cottonhouse

CARIBBEAN - THE GRENADINES (PALM ISLAND)

Palm Island

Palm Island

Tel: +1 954 481 8787
www.condenastjohansens.com/palmisland

CARIBBEAN - TURKS & CAICOS ISLANDS (PARROT CAY)

Parrot Cay by COMO

P.O. Box 164, Providenciales

Tel: +1 649 946 7788
www.condenastjohansens.com/parrotcay

CARIBBEAN - TURKS & CAICOS ISLANDS (PROVIDENCIALES)

Beach House Turks and Caicos

Lower Bight Road 218, Grace Bay Beach, Providenciales

Tel: +1 649 946 5800
www.condenastjohansens.com/turksandcaicos

CARIBBEAN - TURKS & CAICOS ISLANDS (PROVIDENCIALES)

Gansevoort Turks + Caicos, a Wymara Resort

Lower Bight Road, Grace Bay Beach, Providenciales

Tel: +1 649 941 7555
www.condenastjohansens.com/gansevoorttc

CARIBBEAN - TURKS & CAICOS ISLANDS (PROVIDENCIALES)

Grace Bay Club

Grace Bay Circle Road, P.O. Box 128, Grace Bay, Providenciales

Tel: +1 649 946 5050
www.condenastjohansens.com/gracebayclub

CARIBBEAN - TURKS & CAICOS ISLANDS (PROVIDENCIALES)

Mothershouse

Babalua Beach, Providenciales

Tel: +1 613 266 6799
www.condenastjohansens.com/mothershouse

CARIBBEAN - TURKS & CAICOS ISLANDS (PROVIDENCIALES)

Point Grace

Grace Bay Beach, P.O. Box 700, Providenciales

Tel: +1 649 946 5096
www.condenastjohansens.com/pointgrace

CARIBBEAN - TURKS & CAICOS ISLANDS (PROVIDENCIALES)

Regent Palms, Turks & Caicos

16 Princess Drive, Grace Bay Beach, Providenciales

Tel: +649 946 8666
www.condenastjohansens.com/regentpalms

CARIBBEAN - TURKS & CAICOS ISLANDS (PROVIDENCIALES)

The Tuscany on Grace Bay

P.O. Box 623, Grace Bay Beach, Providenciales

Tel: +1 649 941 4667
www.condenastjohansens.com/thetuscanyresort

CARIBBEAN - TURKS & CAICOS ISLANDS (PROVIDENCIALES)

The Veranda Resort & Residences

Princess Drive, Providenciales

Tel: +1 649 339 5050
www.condenastjohansens.com/verandatci

Hotels - Caribbean & Pacific

Properties listed below can be found in our Recommended Hotels, Inns, Resorts, Spas & Villas – The Americas, Caribbean & Pacific 2013 Guide

CARIBBEAN - TURKS & CAICOS ISLANDS (PROVIDENCIALES)

The West Bay Club

Lower Bight Road, Providenciales

Tel: +1 649 946 8550
www.condenastjohansens.com/thewestbayclub

PACIFIC - FIJI ISLANDS (LABASA)

Nukubati Private Island Great Sea Reef

P.O. Box 1928, Labasa

Tel: +679 603 0919
www.condenastjohansens.com/nukubati

PACIFIC - FIJI ISLANDS (NADI)

The Fiji Orchid

Saweni Beach Road, Lautoka, Nadi

Tel: +679 664 0099
www.condenastjohansens.com/fijiorchid

PACIFIC - FIJI ISLANDS (YAQETA ISLAND)

Navutu Stars Resort

P.O. Box 1838, Lautoka

Tel: +679 664 0553
www.condenastjohansens.com/navutustars

PACIFIC - NEW ZEALAND (NORTH ISLAND)

The Point Villas

The Point, Taupo

Tel: +64 7 377 8002
www.condenastjohansens.com/thepointvillas

PACIFIC - NEW ZEALAND (SOUTH ISLAND)

Bay of Many Coves

Queen Charlotte Sound, Private Bag 382, Picton 7250

Tel: +64 3 5799771
www.condenastjohansens.com/bayofmanycoves

PACIFIC - NEW ZEALAND (SOUTH ISLAND)

Kaimata Retreat

297 Cape Saunders Road, Papanui Inlet, RD2
Portobello, Dunedin 9077

Tel: + 64 3 456 3443
www.condenastjohansens.com/kaimatanz

PACIFIC - VANUATU (EFATE ISLAND)

The Havannah Vanuatu

Samoa Point, P.O. Box 4, Port Vila, Efate Island

Tel: + 678 551 8060
www.condenastjohansens.com/thehavannah

The iPad App
for luxury destinations

Search Find Book

Condé Nast Johansens
hotel, spa and venue application available free on iPad™.

www.condenastjohansens.com

CONDÉ NAST
JOHANSENS
Recommended Hotels and Spas

Wine and Spirit courses from the WSET

required by **professionals**

desired by **enthusiasts**

The **Wine & Spirit Education Trust** has been running a wide range of courses for over 40 years – aimed at different levels from novice to professional. Wherever you are in the world, you can choose to learn on-line in the comfort of your own home, or in a relaxed, friendly classroom with like-minded people wishing to learn more about wines (...and spirits).

For further information or to view the WSET's 3-minute Wine School for a **FREE** introduction to the world of wine please visit

www.WSETglobal.com

Index by Property

Index by Property

0-9

A

B

C

D

E

F

g

Index by Property

H

I

K

L

M

N

O

P

R

S

T

Index by Property / Location

Index by Location

London

Channel Islands

England

Index by Location

F

G

H

K

L

M

N

O

R

S

T

U

W

Ireland

Index by Location / Consortium

Scotland

Wales

Index by Consortium

Ireland's Blue Book

Ireland

THE LEADING HOTELS OF THE WORLD Leading Hotels of the World

England

Ireland

PRIDE OF BRITAIN HOTELS Pride of Britain members

England

Wales

RELAIS & CHÂTEAUX Relais & Châteaux

England

Scotland

Small Luxury Hotels of the World

Channel Islands

England